THE COLLECTOR'S GUIDE TO MONSTER, SCIENCE FICTION AND FANTASY FILM MAGAZINES

by Bob Michelucci

imagine
inc.

THE COLLECTOR'S GUIDE TO MONSTER, SCIENCE FICTION and FANTASY FILM MAGAZINES
©1988 Robert V. Michelucci

Each magazine cover reproduced within this guide is copyrighted © by its respective publisher. Those publishers have been named in every possible case immediately following the magazine title throughout the book.

Cover Design: ©Robert V. Michelucci
Cover Illustration: Jack Davis

Published by Imagine, Inc.
ISBN: 0-911137-06-8
LIBRARY OF CONGRESS NO.: 85-82030

Printed in the United States of America
Published by Imagine, Inc.
First Imagine Inc. printing: February, 1988

ACKNOWLEDGEMENTS

I would like to take this opportunity to thank all of those persons who have helped me to compile this edition of The Collector's Guide.

Extra special thanks go to Tom Skulan of Fantaco, Enterprises who not only wrote a piece for the guide but was also kind enough to lend me a batch of magazines to photograph; Steve Dolnick, an avid collector, who was also instrumental in helping to determine magazine values and who also let me borrow some valuable issues from his collection; Mark Sielski for his generous help and for bringing Fangtastic Creatures to my attention; Gary Dorst, Mark Immonen, Greg Eide, and Joe Koch for providing magazines for copying; Justin Waldstein for sending the proposed cover art for the never printed Best of the Monster Times; and to Forry Ackerman, for once again taking the time to write an introduction to the guide.

I would also like to pass along my best wishes to the many dealers across the country who took the time to fill out the several page questionnaire that was sent to them.

Finally, I want to thank my wife, Diana, for all of her help and support through the years.

The following list names those who have helped in some way to make this book possible. If I have forgotten someone it was purely an oversight and please forgive me.

Forrest J Ackerman
Paul Bucciarelli, Jr.
CINEFANTASTIQUE
CINEFEX
Fred Clarke
Tom Cook
Jack Davis
Steve Dolnick
Gary Dorst
Greg Eide
Eide's Comics
FANGORIA
FANTASTIC FILMS
Tim Ferrante

FILMFAX
Fantaco Enterprises
Friendly Frank's Dist.
Golden Apple Books
Elizabeth Guest
Mark Immonen
Deb Jones
Joseph Koch
Ken Kropf
James Manzella
Diana S. Michelucci
O'Quinn Studios
PREVIEW
Second Genesis

Don Shay
Sam Sherman
Mark Sielski
Tom Skulan
Starlog Press
Michael Stein
Jim Steranko
That's Entertainment
Tony Timpone
Justin Waldstein
Raymond Weber
Sharon Williams
Dolores Wilt

DEDICATION:

To Noni,
Mom,
Dee,
Bobby and Dawn
and
in loving memory
of my
Dad.

TABLE OF CONTENTS

INTRODUCTION

It's been ten years since I first wrote and compiled the original COLLEC-
TOR'S GUIDE TO MONSTER MAGAZINES. At the time the first guide
was published we seemed to see what appeared to be the last days of the
"monster" type film magazines. There was only one still publishing and
that was the ever faithful FAMOUS MONSTERS OF FILMLAND. What
we were beginning to see, however, was a new age of magazines that were
dealing primarily with the science fiction aspect of filmmaking. These new
magazines were now taking advantage of the renewed interest in the Star
Trek television series and then, not too much later, the STAR WARS
phenomenon. With the release and worldwide popularity of STAR WARS
the race was on to see just how many new publishers and new titles could
appear on the newsstands. Just as in the early- to mid-60s when the
"monster film magazine" flooded the market, so then in the latter 70s did
the "science fiction film magazine" take over the newsstand space. Unfor-
tunately for the collector, very few of these magazines were really worth
their cover price, let alone the "fluff" type of press release articles that
were included. Month after month, the same pictures would appear on the
covers of the same titles. It is because of this science fiction following that
we have revamped our current title to include the science fiction, fantasy
and horror film magazine.
   Luckily, there were several new titles that did stand above the rest of the
pack. Most notably was the first of the new magazines to appear called
STARLOG. This title was conceived by two fellows by the names of Kerry
O'Quinn and Norman Jacobs and was written on a much more mature level
than was FM. STARLOG brought both color and the "behind the scenes"
look to the genre. These same publishers also went on to give the world
several additional new titles including the now defunct FUTURE and the
new "champion of the world" in horror film magazines, FANGORIA.
That's right, monsters are back and more gruesome than ever thanks to the
special effects wizardry of makeup artists such as Dick Smith, Rick Baker,
and Tom Savini.
   Some other notable titles included FANTASTIC FILMS, CINEFEX,
CINEFANTASTIQUE (already publishing during the first guide), and
QUESTAR (This author's attempt at SF/Fantasy magazine publishing).
   So, with what looked like the final days for the monster magazine collec-
tor in 1977 turned into even better days ahead.

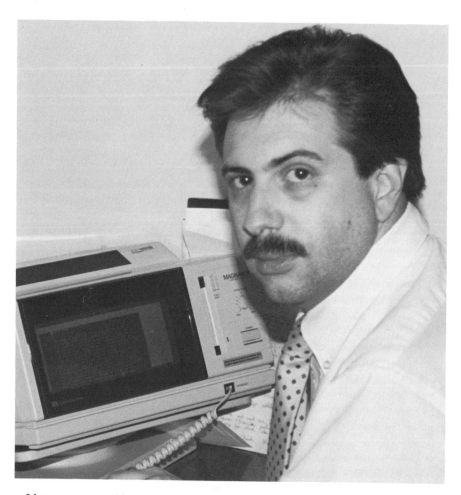

I have attempted here, after numerous requests during the past several years, to update that original Collectors Guide and include the most current values for both the previous magazines listed in that 1977 guide and include cover reproductions and values for *all* magazine titles and their respective issues that have been published from 1977 to the present.

In order to get a "fair market value" for each title and issue, I solicited information from dealers, stores and collectors from across the country. The values set forth in this guide are based on an average from the response to that poll.

It's my hope that once again this guide will become an invaluable reference tool to both collectors and dealers alike.

Enjoy!

Bob Michelucci

A DECADE OF DECAY & DECADENCE
BY
FORREST J ACKERMAN

CAN Such Things Be? as was once asked by Ambrose Bierce, the author whose famous story "The Damned Thing" once appeared in *Weird Tales* magazine in the early 20s, and who disappeared from the ken of humankind in Mexico under mysterious circumstances.

Is it possible that two lustrums have gone with the wand (er, wind) since I wrote the Introduction, "One Glorious Day," for the First Edition of *The Collectors Guide to Monster Magazines*? A decade has passed into history? (Excuse me, feminists in the audience: *her*-story?)

And what hath Father (Mother) Time wrought in the meantime? The filmonsterzine that started it all and was up to its 139th issue at the time: Who would have dreamt that we would not all live to see its 200th issue and 25th Anniversary? I dreamed of editing a dream number for issue 200, a 200-page jam-packed gem-packed collectors item that would be maniacally sought by imagi-movie aficionados in the 21st century, equaled, if not surpassed, by the Silver Anniversary issue. But Fate had a different scenario in store and though I edited 51 issues more (thru 190) the pioneering publication of fantafilms became a memory with #191. (The cover that had been painted for #192 was graciously donated to me for my museum by its artist.)

I don't know how many times since 1958 I've told interested parties and reported in print that the first printing of FMOF was 125,000 copies and that after these sold out the publisher sent it back to press for another 75,000 copies, which also sold out. Nearly 30 years later, in the first issue of a fascinating new filmagazine called *Pure Images*, a journalist named Greg Theakston reports some entirely different figures. According to his information, the first pressrun was 150,000, a phenomenal 90% of which sold, and an additional 117,305 copies were printed and went on sale on the *first of May*. Apparently the reprint (about which I knew nothing till the Theakston report) was kept on sale till mid-July. If this is so, then it may account for the infuriating claims that persist to this day that "FM was not the first movie monster magazine!" Earlier this year some monster fan from Detroit or Cleveland or-?, I frankly don't remember where, broke the record for annoying me by declaring that *three* other monster mags were on the stands in his city before FM came out! According to this latest information by Theakston, I can see where Fan X could be telling the truth: he may never have seen the original FM February release and perhaps saw World Famous Creatures and Journal of Frankenstein and something else before he caught up with the #1 FM *reprint* in July! I can buy that. But can you imagine how galling it would have been, for instance, for some fans to keep insisting to Bela Lugosi that he didn't define Dracula on the stage and then in the 1931 movie. How infuriatingly frustrating if Boris Karloff, for years after he first played the Frankenstein monster, had been challenged, ''Aw, you weren't the first, I saw Lon Chaney Jr. (or Bela Lugosi or Glenn Strange) play Frankenstein before you did!''

I am not always certain of the accuracy of Greg's reports. When he quotes me as saying (around the time of our 5th issue) that I had about 30 authors in my stable and one of them would give a producer a shooting script for a sci-fi or horror film in 3 to 5 weeks under the usual writing time, it seems to me I was representing more like 75 writers at that time (having cut my clientele in half in order to devote editorial time to FM) and only *once* around that time did one of my writers do a movie script: Martin Varno, who wrote *Night of the Blood Beast*. The most erroneous mistake of all is in stating that *I* wanted a skull on the cover of #3 but was outvoted by Warren. *It was the utter opposite.* When Warren wanted to simply put a Halloween type skull on the cover, I recall my argument clearly to this day: ''You could see that kind of a skull in any magic shop! That's not from any movie—if you want a skull, go with the ultimate skull-face: Lon Chaney as the Phantom of the Opera!'' It may have been the only time in our career together that Jim didn't reply, ''You may be right . . . but I'm boss!''

It's fascinating to note how FM has increased in value with the passage of years. Ten years ago that *Guide* estimaed the worth of #1 at $150. Although I personally think the figure somewhat inflated, nevertheless I have known of two issues in recent years commanding a price of $500. And a complete set being advertised for $10,000. (The cinemarchives of the University of Wyoming feature a complete set plus many of the manuscripts for a number of issues.)

The second issue of *Forrest J Ackerman's Monsterland* leapt from cover price to $25 almost overnight. Explanation: the pressrun was shorted. I

never even got the 100 complimentary copies I was contractually entitled to.

This mysterious magazine American oneshot, *House of Horror*, missing from 99% of completists' collections: here's the story on it. There was such a magazine in England. Warren learned they were about to ship a number of copies to America each issue. He didn't want any extra competition so he rushed into print a domestic magazine with the same name, reprinting 4 articles by me with a 5th reprint by Dennis Billows, an assistant of mine at the time. The edition was extremely limited—only 400 copies, if I recall correctly, though on a nice white better stock of paper than FM—because the publisher had only to satisfy certain copyright regulations, such as circulating 200 copies in 5 states (or whatever). This was in 1978. The unsold copies of the "ashcan" edition he gave to me. At one time an assistant (not Billows) stole about 30 copies from me and sold them to a dealer in a nearby city. After the perfidy came to my attention (and the assistant was gone) I bought back my own magazines because they had been sold for far less than I knew they were worth. I thought I had at least 25 left but I just checked and see I'm down to 6. I plan to sell the 6th copy for $75, the 5th for $100, the 4th for $125, the third for $150, the second for $175 and the last for $200. When a fan I know reads this (he's told me he has 10 copies) I imagine he'll hold onto his till mine are gone, then watch for the price to go up 50% or double, as far as I know, he'll control the market.*

In the past 10 years I've seen the rise in popularity of "gorror" films reflected in the decapitations and disembowelments, the bloodbaths in the imagi-movie magazines. Not Ack's-actly my cup of grue but *chacun a son gout*'s of hemoglobin. Incidentally, in the first of my 4 auto-biographical/anecdotal books, *FORREST J ACKERMAN: FAMOUS MONSTER OF FILMLAND*, I remarked that I wished I'd come up with the term "gorror" and had no idea who had. Well, world, my fine friend Randy Palmer has pridefully (and rightly so) informed me that he coined the word. Thanks, Randy!

I'd say more that this time but I've a deadline for producing the second volume of *FJA: FMOF*. See you on Elm Street!

(FORREST)
Ackerman

AUTHOR'S NOTE: After receiving this introduction from Mr. Ackerman, I immediately telephoned him and gave him the astonishing information that the magazine he refers to was valued much higher already than he had planned to sell his copies. Therefore, the pricing shown here for his remaining copies is not in effect. Please contact Mr. Ackerman direct for his current selling prices. 2495 Glendower Ave., Hollywood, CA 90027.

The Behind-the-Scenes Story of Horrorwood's first Filmonster magazine.

COLLECTOR'S EDITION

FORREST J ACKERMAN,
FAMOUS
MONSTER
OF FILMLAND

BEST
BOOK
EVER!

The Behind-the-Scenes
Story of H..rrwood's
first Filmonster magazine

SEE —
A SPECIAL ALUMNI
YEARBOOK SECTION—
FANS TURN PRO

SEE —
INSIDE THE ACKERMANSION

A BRAND NEW
GRAVEYARD EXAMINER

ARE YOU
AMONG THE
MISSING?

BEST BOOK EVER!

The Behind-the-Scenes Story of Horrorwood's first Filmonster magazine.

FORREST J ACKERMAN,
FAMOUS
MONSTER
OF FILMLAND

introduction by VINCENT PRICE! $10.95/FILM

Imagine INC.

WELCOME MONSTER LOVERS!
by Mark Sielski

Remember when *your* collection of FAMOUS MONSTERS, FANTASTIC MONSTERS, HORROR MONSTERS, MAD MONSTERS, and so on ad-nauseum, grew and grew until suddenly it all came to a screeching stop somewhere between your first date and high school senior prom? Finding out what lay beneath Cindy Sue's knit sweater had taken precedence over poor ole Uncle Forry. Without hesitation, most collectors moved on, leaving their FAMOUS MONSTERS collections, fan club membership cards, buttons, sweatshirts, teeshirts, etcetera behind them. Forry and Jim's magic printer's ink, rumored to have been glue, had dried out. Most readers at one time or another, *"Could* Put This Magazine Down!"

For you dear reader, a good boisterous round of salutatory applause. Of the millions of monster magazine readers (1958-1988), it is only thousands who have accepted the challenge of being a collector—preserving for generations to come this phenomenon born as Forry's Folly. Kudos to those poor lost souls who parted with their collections only to later collect with a burning vengeance after realizing their foolishness. Those one time traitors know who they are (this writer included). Shame!

Thirty years ago FM hit the *noose*stands on a cold, snowy February day in New York and Philadelphia. At once it established itself as the "King of the Monster Mags"—forever—no doubts about it. However, a bi-monthly schedule just couldn't satisfy the needs of its voracious readers. And thus was spawned the hellacious offspring known as WORLD FAMOUS CREATURES, MONSTERS AND THINGS, MONSTER PARADE, SHOCK TALES...becoming the supplemental diet of thousands of little monsters. Pandemonium swept the country. Frankenstein and Dracula were running as Republicans. The monster boom ran wildly out of control not slowing down until the mid-70s. By the time the first edition of THE COLLECTORS GUIDE TO MONSTER MAGAZINES (1977) came out, light was made of the fact that FM was the only regularly published monsterzine on the market. A decade later there is still only one—though it's not FM, but FANGORIA. Monster magazine collecting again appears to be at a crossroad.

As this second COLLECTOR'S GUIDE is unleashed on an unsuspecting public—our numbers are mighty—*thousands* strong—awaiting the thrill of the hunt. Competition will be fierce one those long forgotten titles of yesteryear ad even yesterday are revealed.

The fortunate few whose collections are complete may jubilate in fond memories while browsing thru this COLLECTOR'S GUIDE. For those too young to have purchased the rare titles years ago—Good Luck! For those old timers who foolishly failed to heed Big Jim's warning—"The small supply of back issues is disappearing. Buy now, trade later with fellow fans for issues you're missing."—Tough Luck!

A few more thoughts—novices will have years of hard work, but what better job is there than to have the world's greatest hobby! Collectors who have discovered some new titles or missing issues—the thrill of collecting is here again! It's time for all to start looking in those second-hand shops and don't forget to wear an old pair of pants. You'll need 'em when spending countless hours looking for that special issue in the unsorted boxes lying on the comic shop floors. Prepare to be a second-class citizen in the eyes of the dreaded comics dealer. What's this kid's problem? Must come from a broken home? Why is he reading that FM rather than THE AMAZING SPIDERMAN? Beware the high priced, high powered, fast talking dealer who tells you that another copy will never be found. Or better yet, "Make me an offer, I've got thirteen other people wanting to buy it." Don't commit suicide after you pay out a three digit dollar figure only to find the mag a week later for small pocket change. Don't forget to scout out locations to make your deals and trades with other collectors so the wife or parent's don't find out what you're doing. Pizza shops make good locales for the clandestine meetings but make sure the tables are clean before laying down your precious wares! Let's not forget those estranged phone calls from people who have an FM #4 (with a sticker too!) to sell, only to change their minds? last minute. And lets not forget about that mint FM #1 you purchased over the phone that someone while making its way to your possession managed to tape its binding, and cut out a few pix and coupons aka Dr. Jekyll and Mr. Hyde.

You'll soon realize that your best friend in all this business is your postman. Be kind to him because he controls your life-line, and sanity too! No sooner than he leaves that package, you're tearing it open like some crazed zombie in a George Romero flick. From beginning to end, oh what insatiable, delectable fun!!!

One further look into the future...Your collection is complete after years of experiencing the agony and the ecstasy of monster magazine collecting. Your spouse informs you that either the magazine's go or she does...

"ARE WE NOT MEN?"

—Manimals in the ISLE OF LOST SOULS (1933).

COLLECTING FOR FUN AND PROFIT
by Tom Skulan

Collecting the types of magazines listed herein can be an endlessly fascinating hobby and even a lifelong pursuit.

From my vantage point as a collector since 1963 and a dealer since 1973; it seems the best advice to new collectors would be to decide what your collecting goals and interests are before spending large sums on issues you may end up not wanting. Using this guide as a reference, try out some *inexpensive* issues of each magazine to see if it suits your taste. Don't forget the many excellent fanzines (Midnight Marquee, Magick Theatre, Deep Red, Little Shop of Horrors, Cinefan, Cinemacabre and Shock Xpress to name just a few) as they offer a wealth of information not found in general release, newsstand magazines. Plan on spending some time and roughly $50-$200 *reading* and learning about the hobby before *leaping* in. You will find this experience not only educational but money well spent.

Once you have a good feel of what's out there you can decide what to collect. Are you interested in older films or just new ones? Are you mainly interested in horror films, science fiction, or both? Maybe you are interested in collecting material on a particular film, actor or actress. Possibly you will decide to collect entire runs of certain magazines you sampled.

It is important to define your collecting goals for several reasons. First, even a well-endowed checkbook will scarcely allow you to collect *everything*. Often, collectors with this lofty goal end up frustrated, leaving the hobby disillusioned. Second, if you concentrate on collecting those magazines most interesting to you, you will invariably receive more enjoyment from your endeavors. And finally, since almost all fine collections are sold (if not by you then your heirs) it is worth noting that a carefully assembled and protected collection will always bring more than one which is in bits and pieces with no real sense of unity.

Collecting complete runs of titles is the most common type of collecting but some extremely interesting collections have involved variations on the theme. How about collecting *one* copy of each title? This method allows even a collector with a modest budget to assemble, over time, an attractive and unusual collection. You may wish to collect only those issues with a certain monster (most popular for this type of collector is GODZILLA) or even a certain cover artist. For heftier budgets, attempting to collect the first issue of each magazine can be a real challenge and quite possibly an excellent investment.

Investing in monster and sci-fi magazines? There's alot of people doing it. But here's a little secret: collect what you like, carefully build an exciting *collection* and you'll beat the pure investors *everytime*. Why? Because the *investors*, the hard-core *speculators* do not build collections. They build bulk. They do not have an interest in what they are buying nor do they really understand the collectors of these magazines. There is nothing wrong with thinking of your collection as an investment·but if your *only* reason for purchasing magazines is investment, gold, silver or platinum may be a better place for you. Collect for enjoyment first, with possible price gains as a bonus. Monster magazines are a hobby, not a commodity.

Once you are in the habit of buying all your favorite new magazines as they are released you will ultimately begin to seek out some back issues which generally sell for more than cover price, in some instances many multiples of cover price! The prices in this guide are averages of prices charged by *dealers* in this market. They are not what a dealer will pay you for your issues but rather a guide to what type of pricing currently exists in the marketplace. What a dealer will pay you depends on a variety of factors including demand (if the dealer has any customers for what you have), needed profit margin (dealers must make a profit on what they sell to pay rent, utilities, advertising, taxes, salaries, etc.) and supply (how readily available is what you're offering). Because these factors vary widely from dealer to dealer, it would not be unusual to offer an issue to 3 dealers and receive 3 totally different offers!

Should you pay $100 for an issue because it lists in this guide for $100? That is entirely up to you. If it's worth $100 to *you*, yes! If not, no. Remember that the prices listed are frozen in time forever in the typeset of this book. The market isn't. Just a few months from now some of the values listed in this guide will be too high, some too low.

If you have been searching for 10 years for a copy of a certain magazine that lists here for $50 but is being offered to you for $125 you may very well decide to buy it. Conversely you may find magazines listed at $125 available for $50. Use this guide for what it is. A guide, an educational tool. Not a bible. Ultimately the true value of any magazine is what a collector is willing to pay, regardless of the price listed.

Back issue magazines may be attained in a variety of ways. Send for some catalogs and develop relationships with good dealers. When you find those dealers you like, hang on to them as they will be your best sources of new material and correct information. Go to flea markets and garage sales—often rare issues turn up at junk prices. Comic book stores are terrific sources as monster and sci-fi mags are not their primary market and often runs or collectins of scarce issues can be purchased for a fraction of their value. The more adventurous collector may decide to run classified ads in local papers or in some of the film magazines themselves. This can be expensive and time consuming but many collectors have had good results. It's hit or miss. Just remember the responsibility you are entailing when you take out an ad offering to buy something from the public!

As your collection grows it is advisable to protect it in some way. Magazine protective bags are an ideal way to store your issues and keep out dust, dirt and humidity. They are available in both regular style or special "mylar" style (for archival storage). Backing boards can be inserted into the bag behind the magazine to offer extra support but generally magazines don't need it. Specially designed boxes with lids and die cut handles are available which make storage of your bagged collection more orderly and transportable. These supplies are inexpensive and readily available by mail or at comic book stores.

Now that you have your collection bagged, sorted and boxed, you should take one final step. Keep a notebook listing what you have. Then as you purchase new magazines enter them into the log. Why do this? Simple. If your collection is stolen, destroyed, or lost you have a permanent record. If you keep track of price paid, where purchased and the invoice number it will go a long way towards re-imbursement from your insurance company (ask them about special coverage) in the event of a fire or theft. Very few collectors, even those with huge collections, keep logs. Don't make the same mistake. On the lighter side, your log will prevent you from buying duplicates and is an interesting document of how your collection has developed. Even if you ignore everything else in this article. Start a log. NOW!

Collecting can provide you with many hours of enjoyment. Proceed slowly, collect what you enjoy and you will develop a fine collection. Good Luck!

"ONE COLLECTOR'S STORY"
by Steve Dolnick

It all began for me in 1963. A group of kids gathered around the front of my apartment building. Everyone brought along their monster magazines. I brought the Famous Monsters 1964 yearbook (FM yearbooks appeared during the summer of the previous year). I was 7-years-old then, and the kids ranged in age from 6 to 12 years old.There were other FM's, Castle of Frankenstein's, Mad and Horror Monsters. To this day, I wish I could remember which issues were there, on the sidewalk, being tossed around and examined. It was a great day.

In those days, while people were still complaining about the price of comic books going from 10 cents to 12 cents, getting 35 cents to 50 cents from your parents for a monster magazine was tough for a 7-year-old. I remember when I was ill, I told my mom to buy me a monster magazine to read while I was bedridden. She bought me Castle of Frankenstein #4. I was happy, but I liked Famous Monsters better.

By the time I was 10-years-old (1966), I had a small collection, but was able to pick up every new issue of FM from that point on. By 1970, I began attempting to complete my set of FM by seeking back issues. Finally, in 1972, I completed my set. The last issues I needed were FM #3 and FM #4. They were difficult to find back then too!

Sometime in the early 1970's, I noticed a few things that puzzled me. First, FM #2 had no month listed. FM #1 was Feb. 1958 and FM #3 was Apr. 1959. When did FM #2 appear? I've spoken to individuals who had picked up FM on the newsstands since #1, and I've gotten conflicting answers. It seems to have appeared closer to #1 than #3. Exactly which month? I still do not know. The second item that puzzled me was the different covers of FM #7 that appeared in the "Back Issues" department. I had the WOR-TV version, because I lived in the New York area. When I called up Warren Publishing, I was told that there were three versions, distributed to different parts of the country. Also, since then, I found that there were copies of FM #4 and FM #6 with stickers attached. Being a completionist, I had to have them all!

Aside from collecting the magazine, I got involved in other ways. After numerous attempts, my name finally appeared in the Mystery Photo department of FM #88. The trick was to send a reply quickly! Later on, I submitted my photo, which appeared in FM #99. I wanted to appear in FM #100, but my timing was off when I mailed it in. I appear in the photo with my younger brother Craig. What a thrill!

The next stage in my collecting career was upgrading the condition of my collection. I've found that there are two types of collectors—the completionist and the high-grade bug. I chose to be both. Many years have since passed. I was now married and working, so I had some money to invest. If you think it's tough to get early monster magazines, try finding them in a high-grade condition. Every time I found an FM in better shape than my best copy, I bought it. I wound up with many duplicate copies of most early issues (I already had Very Fine to Mint copies from #31 up). Of course, I continued buying the current issues when they appeared.

Years had passed, and when I bought a house, there were endless expenses. My wife Mae suggested that I sell my duplicate copies. I agreed and chose to advertise in a local newspaper. I sold so many magazines that I felt I priced everything too low. Too bad there was no current Monster Price Guide at the time. Another item of interest to me was that people were requesting other magazines such as World Famous Creatures, Monster Parade, etc.

For the next few years I began investing in the "rare" monster magazines. I called comic book shops across the USA and Canada, and bought all of the rare magazines I could find, or afford. Over the past four years, I've come to some conclusions in reference to the scarcity of monster magazines. The following is a sample listing of the scarcity of a few types of monster magazines. This should not be looked at as factual. It's just according to my personal experience. The rarest of each title is listed first:

Famous Monsters	Monster Parade	W.F.C.	Monsters & Things
#7 with red Lucky 7 stamped inside	#1	#2	#2
#6 with sticker	#3	#1	#1
#4 with sticker	#4	#3	
#4	#2	#4	
#3			
#5			
#6			

There are too many qualifying factors involved to describe here, so I won't discuss them now. For example, it's tougher to find FM #3 than it is to find FM #11, but it's tougher to find a MINT copy of FM #11 than it is to find a MINT copy of FM #3. Therefore, my scarcity listings do not take condition into account. These listings have some correlation to pricing, but the public still tends to seek lower numbers. Therefore, first issues usually command the highest price. Most dealers I've spoken to have agreed that they've seen more copies of FM #1 than FM #21, yet FM #1 commands a much higher price. Supply and demand are the key factors in determining pricing.

There's one subject I'd like to clear up. Monster Parade had only four issues, not six. If there are copies of #5 and #6, they haven't surfaced yet. The reason for the confusion lies within the fact that the first issue reads Vol. 2, No. 6 inside. Monster Parade must have been converted from another magazine. In the editorial department, the Old Ghoul states that it's the first issue. Also, this magazine is dated earlier than Monster Parade #2. One more note on Monster Parade—the paper stock is cheap. I've never seen a copy better than Very Fine in condition. If anyone knows what it was called before Monster Parade, or if you have a #5, please inform this price guide.

Thank goodness this monster magazine price guide has appeared. There was a strong need for one. The only disadvantage is that nobody will sell me FM #5 for $10 anymore! However, the advantages, certainly outweigh the disadvantages. I hope to see updates in the future.

GRADING GUIDE & PRICING INFORMATION

The following information is meant to help both the collector and the seller in determining the actual worth of any given magazine based on the type of shape the particular magazine is in at the time of its evaluation.

Although most magazine collectors values are based mainly on how new a magazine may look, other determining factors do come into play. In many instances a certain issue of a certain title may just not be available in the best possible condition and so in this case a value will be based primarily on supply and demand with the actual visual appeal of the particular issue becoming secondary.

All of the pricing found in this guide is based on an average of what each title is actually being sold and paid for across the country. Anyone who shops around, however, may occasionally find some bargains, but watch out because there are just as many bargains that become ''rip-offs''! Know your collection.

Again, in pricing, rarity is not always the most determining factor. As an example, using the title FAMOUS MONSTERS OF FILMLAND, it seems that the rarest issue is #4 (especially with the ride the Ghouls Eye sticker on it) but it's the first issue that still commands the highest price due to demand. This is true even though issues 3, 5, and 6 are still harder to find in top shape than the first. It's also extremely rare to find a perfect copy of #'s 11 and 12. Those damn covers kept falling off!

In any case the following list should be used only as a helping hand in determining the actual grade or condition that the magazine in question may be in.

MINT: This should be a *perfect* magazine. The cover has a full shine or lustre, it's corners and/edges are sharp and its pages are still like new. There should be no signs of wear or of aging and should have absolutely no imperfections. In other words, this magazine should be indistinguishable from any brand new magazine fresh off the corner newsstand.

FINE: This magazine may show a small bit of wear on the cover and spine, but should still be clean and flattened. There shouldn't be any signs of cover defacement and/or repair by tape (this includes the spine of the issue). The corners may show slight signs of rounding, however this is a nice looking issue at first glance.

GOOD: This grading is used for a still complete but very worn magazine. The cover is showing definite signs of wear including minor tears and a rounded spine. There should still be little or no evidence of tape or brittle pages. All coupons should still be intact.

FAIR: A magazine judged to be in this condition may have a slightly soiled and/or damaged cover with possibly some corners gone from wear. Although it is an issue that shoule be still intact, it may have a multitude of problems and may be missing a mail order coupon or two. The use of tape to attempt repair on the cover or inside pages will more than likely be present.

POOR: To put it bluntly, this type of magazine rarely has any collectible value unless it is to complete ones collection while looking for a better copy. We're talking about a magazine that really looks like it should have been tossed into the trash (or perhaps was and then retrieved). It is the absolute last word in poor shape. The cover is terribly worn and scribbled on, taped, dogeared corners (if they're still there!) and probably coffee stained. The inside doesn't look much better... ripped pages or even missing pages, loose pages, and pages missing coupons. These can usually be found in the "Bargain Bin."

This book is listing only values for MINT and GOOD copies. To determine the values for the other gradings, I would suggest to deduct approximately twenty percent (20%) from the mint value for each downgrading.

THE PRICE GUIDE

ADVENTURES IN HORROR

Stanley Publications, Inc.
October, 1970-December 1970

#1
MINT $20.00
GOOD $12.50

#2
MINT $17.00
GOOD $10.00

ALIEN

Warren Publishing Company
December, 1979

MINT $4.00
GOOD: $2.25

AMAZING FORRIES

(One shot)
Metropolis Publications
November, 1976

MINT $25.00
GOOD $11.50

BLACK ZOO

(One shot)
Charlton Publications
Fall, 1963

MINT $17.50
GOOD $10.00

CASTLE OF FRANKENSTEIN

Gothic Castle Publishing Company
Publisher/Editor: Calvin T. Beck
January, 1962-June, 1975

#1
MINT $35.00
GOOD $15.00

#2
MINT $25.00
GOOD $15.00

#3
MINT $25.00
GOOD $15.00

#4
MINT $20.00
GOOD $11.00

#5
MINT $16.00
GOOD $10.00

#6
MINT $15.00
GOOD $10.00

#7
MINT $15.00
GOOD $10.00

#8	#9	#10
MINT $15.00	MINT $15.00	MINT $15.00
GOOD $10.00	GOOD $10.00	GOOD $10.00

#11	#12	#13
MINT $27.50	MINT $18.00	MINT $18.00
GOOD $20.00	GOOD $11.50	GOOD $11.50

#14	#15	#16
MINT $18.00	MINT $18.00	MINT $18.00
GOOD $11.50	GOOD $11.50	GOOD $11.50

21

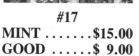

#17
MINT $15.00
GOOD . . . . . . $ 9.00

#18
MINT $15.00
GOOD . . . . . . $ 9.00

#19
MINT $15.00
GOOD . . . . . . $ 9.00

#20
MINT $15.00
GOOD . . . . . . $ 9.00

#21
MINT $17.50
GOOD $10.25

#22
MINT $17.50
GOOD $10.25

#23
MINT $17.50
GOOD $10.25

#24
MINT $18.00
GOOD $11.50

#25
MINT $18.00
GOOD $11.50

#8.5 1967 ANNUAL
MINT $30.00
GOOD $22.00

CHILLING MONSTER TALES

(One Shot)
MM Publishing, Ltd.
August, 1966

#1
MINT $15.00
GOOD $10.00

CINEFANTASTIQUE

Frederick S. Clarke
(Fanzine mimeographed edition—at least five exist. Shown is a representative cover.)

Values remain undetermined.

CINEFANTASTIQUE

Frederick S. Clarke,
Fall, 1970-Present

#1
MINT $37.00
GOOD $16.00

#2
MINT $25.00
GOOD $11.00

#3
MINT $20.00
GOOD . . . . . . $ 9.00

#4
MINT $16.00
GOOD . . . . . . $ 7.50

#5
MINT $8.00
GOOD $3.50

#6
MINT $8.00
GOOD $3.50

#7
MINT $8.00
GOOD $3.50

#8
MINT $8.00
GOOD $3.50

#9
MINT $8.00
GOOD $3.50

#10
MINT $8.00
GOOD $3.50

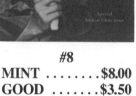

#11
MINT $8.00
GOOD $3.50

#12
MINT $8.00
GOOD $3.50

#13
MINT $8.00
GOOD $3.50

#14
MINT $8.00
GOOD $3.50

#15
MINT $8.00
GOOD $3.50

#16
MINT $8.00
GOOD $3.50

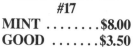

#17	#18	#19
MINT $8.00	MINT $8.00	MINT $22.00
GOOD $3.50	GOOD $3.50	GOOD $10.00

#20	#21	#22
MINT $8.00	MINT $8.00	MINT. $17.00
GOOD. $6.00	GOOD $3.50	GOOD. . . . . .$ 9.00

#23	#24	#25
MINT $8.00	MINT $25.00	MINT $7.00
GOOD $3.50	GOOD $13.50	GOOD. $3.00
	(First double issue)	

#26
MINT $17.50
GOOD $10.00
(double issue)

#27
MINT $7.00
GOOD $3.00

#28
MINT $15.00
GOOD ..... $ 8.50
(double issue)

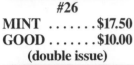

#29
MINT $7.00
GOOD $3.00

#30
MINT $7.00
GOOD $3.00

#31
MINT $7.00
GOOD $3.00

#32
MINT $11.00
GOOD ...... $ 6.00
(double issue)

#33
MINT $7.00
GOOD $3.00

#34
MINT $7.00
GOOD $3.00

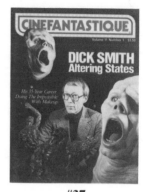

#35
MINT $7.00
GOOD. $3.00

#36
MINT $7.00
GOOD $3.00

#37
MINT $7.00
GOOD $3.00

#38
MINT $7.00
GOOD. $3.00

#39
MINT $7.00
GOOD. $3.00

#40
MINT $7.00
GOOD. $3.00

#41
MINT $7.00
GOOD. $3.00

#42
MINT $11.00
GOOD. . . . . . .$ 6.00
(double issue)

#43
MINT $7.00
GOOD. $3.00

#44
MINT $20.00
GOOD $12.00
(double issue, two covers)

#45
MINT $7.00
GOOD $3.00

#46
MINT $17.00
GOOD . . . . $ 9.00

#47
MINT $7.00
GOOD $3.00

#48
MINT $7.00
GOOD $3.00

#49
MINT $12.00
GOOD . . . . $ 7.50
(double issue)

#50
MINT $7.00
GOOD $3.00

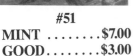

#51

MINT $7.00
GOOD $3.00

#52

MINT $12.00
GOOD $7.50
(double issue)

#53

MINT $7.00
GOOD $3.00

#54

MINT $7.00
GOOD $3.00

#55

MINT $7.00
GOOD $3.00

#56

MINT $7.00
GOOD $3.00

#57

MINT $7.00
GOOD $3.00

#58

MINT $7.00
GOOD $3.00

#59

MINT $7.00
GOOD $3.00

#60
MINT $7.00
GOOD $3.00

#61
MINT $7.00
GOOD $3.00

#62
MINT $7.00
GOOD $3.00

#63
MINT $15.00
GOOD . . . . . . $ 8.50

#64
MINT $7.00
GOOD $3.00

#65
MINT $7.00
GOOD $3.00

COVER
PHOTO
NOT
AVAILABLE
AT
PRESSTIME

#66
MINT $7.00
GOOD $3.00

#67
MINT $7.00
GOOD $3.00

CINEFEX

Don Shay Publishing
March, 1980-Present

#1
MINT $15.00
GOOD . . . .$ 7.00

#2
MINT $12.00
GOOD . . . . . .$ 5.50

#3
MINT $10.00
GOOD . . . . . .$ 4.25

#4
MINT **$10.00**
GOOD . . . . . . **$ 4.25**

#5
MINT **$9.00**
GOOD **$4.00**

#6
MINT **$8.00**
GOOD **$3.75**

#7
MINT **$7.00**
GOOD **$3.25**

#8
MINT **$6.50**
GOOD **$2.75**

#9
MINT **$6.00**
GOOD **$2.50**

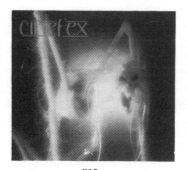

#10
MINT $5.50
GOOD $2.25

#11
MINT $5.00
GOOD $2.00

#12
MINT $5.00
GOOD $2.00

#13
MINT $5.00
GOOD $2.00

#14
MINT $5.00
GOOD $2.00

#15
MINT $5.00
GOOD $2.00

#16
MINT $5.00
GOOD $2.00

#17
MINT $5.00
GOOD $2.00

#18
MINT $5.00
GOOD $2.00

#19
MINT $5.00
GOOD $2.00

#20
MINT $7.50
GOOD $3.50

#21
MINT $8.00
GOOD $3.75

#22
MINT $8.00
GOOD $3.75

#23
MINT $8.00
GOOD $3.75

#24
MINT $8.00
GOOD $3.75

#25
MINT $8.00
GOOD $3.75

#26
MINT $8.00
GOOD $3.75

#27
MINT $8.00
GOOD $3.75

#28
MINT $8.00
GOOD $3.75

#29
MINT $8.00
GOOD $3.75

#30
MINT $8.00
GOOD $3.75

#31
MINT $8.00
GOOD $3.75

CINEMAGIC

Cinema Enterprises
1972-1979
(Eleven issues published
by Don Dohler before O'Quinn
Studios version)
Shown is a representative issue

ALL ISSUES
MINT $10.00
GOOD . . . . . $ 6.00

CINEMAGIC

O'Quinn Studios
1979-1987

CANCELLED AFTER ISSUE #37

#1

MINT $12.50
GOOD $6.00

#2

MINT $5.00
GOOD $3.00

#3

MINT $5.00
GOOD $3.00

#4

MINT $5.00
GOOD $3.00

#5

MINT $5.00
GOOD $3.00

#6

MINT $5.00
GOOD $3.00

#7

MINT $5.00
GOOD $3.00

#8

MINT $5.00
GOOD $3.00

#9

MINT $5.00
GOOD $3.00

#10

MINT $5.00
GOOD $3.00

#11

MINT $5.00
GOOD $3.00

#12

MINT $5.00
GOOD $3.00

#13

MINT $5.00
GOOD $3.00

#14

MINT $5.00
GOOD $3.00

#15

MINT $5.00
GOOD $3.00

#16

MINT $5.00
GOOD $3.00

#17	#18	#19
MINT $5.00	MINT $5.00	MINT $5.00
GOOD $3.00	GOOD $3.00	GOOD $3.00

#20	#21	#22
MINT $5.00	MINT $5.00	MINT $5.00
GOOD $3.00	GOOD $3.00	GOOD $3.00

#23	#24	#25
MINT $5.00	MINT $5.00	MINT $5.00
GOOD $3.00	GOOD $3.00	GOOD $3.00

40

#26

MINT $5.00
GOOD $3.00

#27

MINT $5.00
GOOD $3.00

#28

MINT $5.00
GOOD $3.00

#29

MINT $5.00
GOOD $3.00

#30

MINT $5.00
GOOD $3.00

#31

MINT $4.00
GOOD $2.50

#32

MINT $4.00
GOOD $2.50

#33

MINT $4.00
GOOD $2.50

#34

MINT $4.00
GOOD $2.50

CINEMA ODYSSEY

(One shot)
Roger Wong
1981

#1
MINT $3.00
GOOD $1.75

CLOSE ENCOUNTERS OF THE THIRD KIND

(One shot)
Warren Publishing Company
1977

#1
MINT $5.00
GOOD $1.50

COLLECTORS GUIDE TO MONSTER MAGAZINES

Dick Z Associates
1977, 1978

Pre-publication Edition	First Printing	Second Printing
MINT $60.00	MINT $35.00	MINT $20.00
GOOD $40.00	GOOD $20.00	GOOD . . . . . . $ 8.00

CRACKED'S COLLECTOR'S EDITION: THOSE CRACKED MONSTERS (One shot)

Major Magazines, Inc.
September, 1978

#1
MINT $5.25
GOOD $1.50

CURSE OF FRANKENSTEIN/ HORROR OF DRACULA (One shot)

Warren Publishing Company
1964

#1
MINT $10.00
GOOD $4.50

DAWN OF THE DEAD POSTERBOOK

(One shot)
MW Communications
1979

Without Movie Title on inner poster:	With Movie Title on inner poster:	(Unsigned)
MINT $50.00	MINT $35.00	MINT $30.00
GOOD $35.00	signed by Savini)	GOOD $16.50

DICK SMITH'S MONSTER MAKE-UP HANDBOOK

(One shot)
Warren Publishing Company
1965

MINT $35.00
GOOD $10.00

DRACULA CLASSIC

(One shot)
Eerie Publications, Inc.
1976

MINT $4.25
GOOD $1.50

DRACULA '79

(One shot)
Warren Publishing Company
1979

MINT $4.50
GOOD $1.50

#1
MINT $500.00
GOOD $325.00

(British Edition) #1
MINT $400.00
GOOD $250.00

#2
MINT $125.00
GOOD $75.00

COVER
PHOTO
NOT
AVAILABLE
AT
PRESSTIME

(British Edition) #2
MINT $125.00
GOOD $75.00

#3
MINT $225.00
GOOD $150.00

#4
MINT $400.00
GOOD $250.00
(Ghouls Eye Sticker)

45

#4
MINT $300.00
GOOD $200.00

#5
MINT $200.00
GOOD $125.00

(M.T. Graves Sticker)
MINT $300.00
GOOD $195.00

#6
MINT $175.00
GOOD $115.00

(Roland Cover) #7*
MINT 125.00
GOOD.....$ 85.00

(Tomorrow's Monsters)*
MINT $115.00
GOOD.....$ 75.00

(Zacherley Cover) *
MINT $150.00
GOOD $100.00
*Add $50.00 to any of
the above values if the
Lucky 7 imprint
appears on the inside.

#8
MINT $125.00
GOOD.....$ 85.00

#9
MINT $110.00
GOOD.....$ 70.00

#10
MINT $100.00
GOOD......$ 65.00

#11
MINT.......$175.00
GOOD.....$ 95.00

#12
MINT.......$175.00
GOOD.....$ 95.00

#13
MINT $140.00
GOOD......$ 65.00

#14
MINT $90.00
GOOD......$60.00

#15
MINT $135.00
GOOD......$ 85.00

#16
MINT $75.00
GOOD.......$45.00

#17
MINT $75.00
GOOD.......$45.00

#18
MINT $75.00
GOOD.......$45.00

#19
MINT $75.00
GOOD $45.00

#20
MINT $75.00
GOOD $45.00

#21
MINT $145.00
GOOD ..... $ 95.00

#22
MINT $145.00
GOOD ..... $ 95.00

#23
MINT $70.00
GOOD $35.00

#24
MINT $70.00
GOOD $35.00

#25
MINT $70.00
GOOD $35.00

#26
MINT $70.00
GOOD $35.00

#27
MINT $70.00
GOOD $35.00

#28
MINT $65.00
GOOD $30.00

#29
MINT $60.00
GOOD $30.00

#30
MINT $70.00
GOOD $40.00

#31
MINT $45.00
GOOD $20.00

#32
MINT $40.00
GOOD $17.50

#33
MINT $30.00
GOOD $15.00

#34
MINT $20.00
GOOD $12.00

#35
MINT $10.00
GOOD . . . . . . $ 4.50

#36
MINT $7.50
GOOD $3.50

#37
MINT $7.50
GOOD $3.50

#38
MINT $70.00
GOOD. $38.00

#39
MINT $7.50
GOOD $3.50

#40
MINT $7.50
GOOD $3.50

#41
MINT $7.50
GOOD $3.50

#42
MINT $7.50
GOOD $3.50

#43
MINT $7.50
GOOD $3.50

#44
MINT $7.50
GOOD $3.50

#45
MINT $7.50
GOOD $3.50

#46
MINT $17.50
GOOD $13.50

#47
MINT $7.50
GOOD $3.50

#48
MINT $17.50
GOOD $13.50

#49
MINT $16.00
GOOD $12.50

#50
MINT $15.00
GOOD . . . . . . $ 8.00

#51
MINT $7.25
GOOD $3.00

#52
MINT $17.25
GOOD $13.00

#53
MINT $7.25
GOOD $3.00

#54
MINT $7.25
GOOD $3.00

#55
MINT $7.25
GOOD $3.00

#56
MINT $55.00
GOOD $22.50

#57
MINT $7.25
GOOD $3.00

#58
MINT $7.25
GOOD $3.00

#59
MINT $17.50
GOOD . . . . $ 8.00

#60
MINT $7.25
GOOD $3.00

#61
MINT $7.25
GOOD $3.00

#62
MINT $7.25
GOOD $3.00

#63
MINT $7.25
GOOD $3.00

#64	#65	#66
MINT $7.25	MINT $7.25	MINT $7.25
GOOD $3.00	GOOD $3.00	GOOD $3.00

#67	#68	#69
MINT $7.25	MINT $7.25	MINT $7.25
GOOD $3.00	GOOD $3.00	GOOD $3.00

IT HAS BEEN ESTABLISHED THAT MONSTER WORLD 1-10 HAVE BEEN REDESIGNATED FAMOUS MONSTERS 70-79. PLEASE REFER TO MONSTER WORLD FOR THESE VALUES.

See
MONSTER
WORLD
(Warren)

See
MONSTER
WORLD
(Warren)

See MONSTER WORLD (Warren)	See MONSTER WORLD (Warren)	See MONSTER WORLD (Warren)
See MONSTER WORLD (Warren)	See MONSTER WORLD (Warren)	See MONSTER WORLD (Warren)

See MONSTER WORLD (Warren)		

#80
MINT $10.00
GOOD . . . . $ 4.75

#81
MINT $10.00
GOOD $4.75

#82
MINT $30.00
GOOD $17.50

#83
MINT $10.00
GOOD $4.75

#84
MINT $10.00
GOOD $4.75

#85
MINT $10.00
GOOD $4.75

#86
MINT $10.00
GOOD $4.75

#87
MINT $9.50
GOOD $4.50

#88
MINT $9.50
GOOD $4.50

#89
MINT $9.00
GOOD $4.50

#90
MINT $9.00
GOOD $4.50

#91
MINT........$17.00
GOOD........$9.00

#92
MINT $14.50
GOOD......$ 9.00

#93
MINT $14.50
GOOD........$9.00

#94
MINT $9.00
GOOD $4.50

#95
MINT $9.00
GOOD $4.50

#96
MINT $9.00
GOOD $4.50

#97
MINT $6.00
GOOD $2.50

#98
MINT $6.00
GOOD $2.50

#99
MINT $6.00
GOOD $2.50

#100
MINT $20.00
GOOD...... $14.50

#101
MINT $6.00
GOOD $2.50

#102
MINT $6.00
GOOD $2.50

#103
MINT $6.00
GOOD $2.50

#104
MINT $6.00
GOOD $2.50

#105
MINT $6.00
GOOD $2.50

#106
MINT $6.00
GOOD $2.50

#107
MINT $6.00
GOOD $2.50

#108
MINT $16.00
GOOD $12.50

#109	#110	#111
MINT $6.00	MINT $6.00	MINT $6.00
GOOD $2.50	GOOD $2.50	GOOD $2.50

#112	#113	#114
MINT $6.00	MINT $6.00	MINT $100.00
GOOD $2.50	GOOD $2.50	GOOD.......$45.00

#115	#116	#117
MINT $5.00	MINT $5.00	MINT $5.00
GOOD $2.00	GOOD $2.00	GOOD $2.00

#118

MINT $15.00
GOOD $9.00

#119

MINT $5.00
GOOD $2.00

#120

MINT $5.00
GOOD $2.00

#121

MINT $5.00
GOOD $2.00

#122

MINT $5.00
GOOD $2.00

#123

MINT $5.00
GOOD $2.00

#124

MINT $5.00
GOOD $2.00

#125

MINT $5.00
GOOD $2.00

#126

MINT $5.00
GOOD $2.00

#127
MINT $5.00
GOOD $2.00

#128
MINT $5.00
GOOD $2.00

#129
MINT $5.00
GOOD $2.00

#130
MINT $5.00
GOOD $2.00

#131
MINT $5.00
GOOD $2.00

#132
MINT $5.00
GOOD $2.00

#133
MINT $5.00
GOOD $2.00

#134
MINT $5.00
GOOD $2.00

#135
MINT $5.00
GOOD $2.00

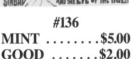

#136	#137	#138
MINT $5.00	MINT $5.00	MINT $5.00
GOOD $2.00	GOOD $2.00	GOOD $2.00

#139	#140	#141
MINT $5.00	MINT $4.50	MINT $4.50
GOOD $2.00	GOOD $1.75	GOOD $1.75

#142	#143	#144
MINT $4.50	MINT $4.50	MINT $4.50
GOOD $1.75	GOOD $1.75	GOOD $1.75

#145
MINT $4.50
GOOD $1.75

#146
MINT $10.00
GOOD . . . . . . $ 6.00

#147
MINT $4.50
GOOD $1.75

#148
MINT $4.50
GOOD $1.75

#149
MINT $4.50
GOOD $1.75

#150
MINT $4.50
GOOD $1.75

#151
MINT $4.50
GOOD $1.75

#152
MINT $4.50
GOOD $1.75

#153
MINT $4.50
GOOD $1.75

#154
MINT $4.50
GOOD $1.75

#155
MINT $4.50
GOOD $1.75

#156
MINT $4.50
GOOD $1.75

#157
MINT $4.50
GOOD $1.75

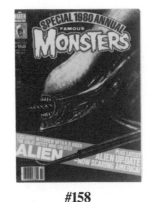

#158
MINT $4.50
GOOD $1.75

#159
MINT $4.50
GOOD $1.75

#160
MINT $4.25
GOOD $1.50

#161
MINT $4.25
GOOD $1.50

#162
MINT $4.25
GOOD $1.50

#163
MINT $25.00
GOOD $16.50

#164
MINT $4.25
GOOD $1.50

#165
MINT $4.25
GOOD $1.50

#166
MINT $4.25
GOOD $1.50

#167
MINT $4.25
GOOD $1.50

#168
MINT $4.25
GOOD $1.50

#169
MINT $4.25
GOOD $1.50

#170
MINT $4.25
GOOD $1.50

#171
MINT $4.25
GOOD $1.50

#172	#173	#174
MINT $4.25	MINT $4.25	MINT $4.25
GOOD $1.50	GOOD $1.50	GOOD $1.50

#175	#176	#177
MINT $4.25	MINT $4.25	MINT $4.25
GOOD $1.50	GOOD $1.50	GOOD $1.50

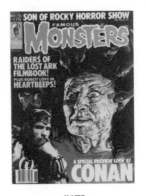

#178	#179	#180
MINT $4.25	MINT $4.25	MINT $4.00
GOOD $1.50	GOOD $1.50	GOOD $1.25

#181

MINT $4.00
GOOD $1.25

#182

MINT $4.00
GOOD $1.25

#183

MINT $4.00
GOOD $1.25

#184

MINT $4.00
GOOD $1.25

#185

MINT $4.00
GOOD $1.25

#186

MINT $4.00
GOOD $1.25

#187

MINT $4.00
GOOD $1.25

#188

MINT $4.00
GOOD $1.25

#189

MINT $4.00
GOOD $1.25

66

#190
MINT $7.50
GOOD $4.00

#191
MINT $9.00
GOOD $5.50

1962 YEARBOOK
MINT $125.00
GOOD . . . . . $ 85.00

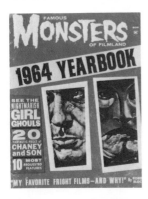

1964 YEARBOOK
MINT $50.00
GOOD $32.50

1965 YEARBOOK
MINT $30.00
GOOD $18.75

1966 YEARBOOK
MINT $27.00
GOOD $12.75

1967 YEARBOOK
MINT $17.50
GOOD . . . . . $ 6.25

1968 YEARBOOK
MINT $10.00
GOOD . . . . . $ 6.50

1969 YEARBOOK
MINT $10.00
GOOD . . . . . $ 6.50

1970 YEARBOOK	1971 YEARBOOK	1972 YEARBOOK
MINT $15.00	MINT $20.00	MINT $35.00
GOOD.......$ 7.50	GOOD ......$ 9.50	GOOD $21.75

FAMOUS MONSTERS OF FILMLAND CONVENTION BOOKS

Warren Publishing Company
1974-1975

1974 CONVENTION
MINT $60.00
GOOD........37.50

1975 CONVENTION
MINT........$75.00
GOOD.......$42.00

FAMOUS MONSTERS GAME BOOK

(One shot)
Warren Publishing Company
June, 1982

MINT $7.50
GOOD $2.50

FAMOUS MONSTERS OF FILMLAND PAPERBACKS

Paperback Library/Warren
Publishing Company
June, 1964-June, 1965

#1
MINT $75.00
GOOD $22.50

#2
MINT $75.00
GOOD $22.50

#3
MINT $60.00
GOOD $17.50

FANGTASTIC CREATURES

(One shot)
Maipix Publishing (Tabloid)
1974

No confirmed sales to date.
Value undetermined.
Possible fanzine.

FANGORIA

(Original title was to be
FANTASTICA)
O'Quinn Studios
August, 1979-Present.

(Back issues are currently available
from the publisher. Therefore, we list
only mint values except in those cases
of "sold out" back issues.)

#1
MINT $30.00

#2
MINT . . . . $ 4.00

#3
MINT . . . . $ 4.00

#4
MINT . . . . $ 6.00

#5
MINT . . . . $ 6.00

#6
MINT . . . . $ 4.00

#7
MINT . . . . $ 4.00

#8
MINT . . . . $ 9.00

#9
MINT $75.00
GOOD $55.00

#10
MINT $15.00

#11
MINT . . . . $ 9.00

#12
MINT $15.00

#13
MINT . . . . $ 6.00

#14
MINT . . . . $ 8.00

#15
MINT . . . . $ 4.00

#16
MINT . . . . $ 4.00

#17
MINT . . . . $ 4.00

#18
MINT $10.00

#19
MINT . . . . $ 9.00

#20
MINT $15.00

#21
MINT . . . . $ 9.00

#22
MINT . . . . $ 9.00

#23
MINT . . . . $ 9.00

#24
MINT . . . . $ 9.00

#25
MINT . . . . $ 4.00

#26
MINT . . . . $ 4.00

#27
MINT . . . . $ 4.00

#28
MINT . . . . $ 4.00

#29
MINT . . . . $ 4.00

#30
MINT . . . . $ 4.00

#31
MINT . . . . $ 4.00

#32
MINT . . . . $ 4.00

#33
MINT . . . . $ 4.00

#34
MINT . . . . $ 4.00

#35
MINT . . . . . . $ 4.00

#36
MINT . . . . . . $ 4.00

#37
MINT . . . . . . $ 4.00

#38
MINT . . . . . . $ 4.00

#39
MINT . . . . . . $ 4.00

#40
MINT . . . . . . $ 4.00

#41
MINT . . . . . . $ 4.00

#42
MINT . . . . . . $ 4.00

#43
MINT . . . . . . $ 9.00

#44
MINT . . . . $ 4.00

#45
MINT . . . . $ 4.00

#46
MINT . . . . $ 9.00

#47
MINT . . . . $ 9.00

#48
MINT . . . . $ 4.00

#49
MINT . . . . $ 4.00

#50
MINT . . . . $ 4.00

#51
MINT . . . . $ 4.00

#52
MINT . . . . $ 4.00

#53
MINT . . . . $ 4.00

#54
MINT . . . . $ 4.00

#55
MINT . . . . $ 4.00

#56
MINT . . . . $ 4.00

#57
MINT . . . . $ 4.00

#58
MINT . . . . $ 4.00

#59
MINT . . . . $ 4.00

#60
MINT . . . . $ 4.00

#61
MINT . . . . $ 4.00

#62
MINT . . . . $ 4.00

#63
MINT . . . . $ 4.00

#64
MINT . . . . $ 4.00

#65
MINT . . . . $ 4.00

#66
MINT $4.25

#67
MINT $4.25

#68
MINT $4.25

#69
MINT $4.25

#70
MINT $4.25

BLOODY BEST OF FANGORIA

#1
MINT $20.00
GOOD . . . . . . $ 7.25

#2
MINT $15.00
GOOD . . . . . . $ 6.50

#3
MINT $12.50
GOOD . . . . . . $ 5.25

#4
MINT . . . . $ 9.00
GOOD . . . . . . $ 4.25

#5
MINT . . . . $ 4.50
GOOD . . . . . . $ 1.75

#6
MINT $4.00
GOOD $1.75

FANGORIA
POSTCARDS

#1
MINT $5.00
GOOD $2.75

FANGORIA
POSTER
MAGAZINE

#1
MINT . . . . . . $ 7.25
GOOD . . . . $ 3.00

#2
MINT $5.00
GOOD $3.00

FANTACO

THE MOST WELL-KNOWN AND TRUSTED NAME IN HORROR BOOK AND MAGAZINE MAIL ORDER.

NOW CELEBRATING OUR TENTH YEAR!

CHECK OUR FULL-PAGE ADS IN *EVERY* ISSUE OF *FANGORIA* MAGAZINE!

NOW AVAILABLE!!!
OUR FANTASTIC
10TH ANNIVERSARY CATALOG!

Over 64 pages of obscure books, magazines, fanzines, masks, make-up books and supplies. Heavily illustrated with complete descriptions.

PLUS A BRAND NEW COVER BY CHAS. BALUN!

This catalog is a collector's item itself!

ORDER ONE TODAY!!!
ONLY

$2⁵⁰

Postpaid—*Anywhere!*

ORDER NOW!!!

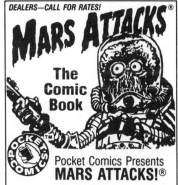

FANTACO
Enterprises Inc.
Publishing • Mail Order • Retail • Conventions
21 Central Avenue • Dept. BOB • Albany, NY 12210
1-518-463-3667

DON'T MISS FANTACON—**September 10 and 11, 1988** at the Governor Nelson A. Rockefeller Empire State Plaza Convention Center. Horror film books, magazines, science fiction, movies, videos, records, comic books, original art and many guests including Forrest J Ackerman, Chas. Balun and John Russo. *Many more to be announced!* Also the world premiere of **Midnight Marquee #37**—the special 208-page 25th anniversary issue!!! *Hundreds of dealer tables!* Be sure to attend—call **1-518-463-3667** for more information!

FANTASTIC FILMS

Blake Publishing Corporation,
Fantastic Films Magazine, Inc.
April, 1978-October, 1985

#1
MINT $10.00
GOOD . . . . . . $ 3.00

#2
MINT $8.00
GOOD $4.00

#3
MINT $6.00
GOOD $3.00

#4
MINT $4.00
GOOD $2.00

#5
MINT $3.00
GOOD $2.00

#6
MINT $2.00
GOOD $1.00

#7
MINT $2.00
GOOD $1.00

#8

MINT $2.00
GOOD $1.00

#9

MINT $8.00
GOOD $5.00

#10

MINT $2.00
GOOD $1.00

#11

MINT $2.00
GOOD $1.00

#12

MINT $2.00
GOOD $1.00

#13

MINT $2.00
GOOD $1.00

#14

MINT $2.00
GOOD $1.00

#15

MINT $2.00
GOOD $1.00

#16

MINT $2.00
GOOD $1.00

#17
MINT $2.00
GOOD $1.00

#18
MINT $2.00
GOOD $1.00

#19
MINT $2.00
GOOD $1.00

#20
MINT $2.00
GOOD $1.00

#21
MINT $2.00
GOOD $1.00

#22
MINT $2.00
GOOD $1.00

#23
MINT $2.00
GOOD $1.00

#24
MINT $2.00
GOOD $1.00

#25
MINT $2.00
GOOD $1.00

COVER
PHOTO
NOT
AVAILABLE
AT
PRESSTIME

#26
MINT $2.00
GOOD $1.00

#27
MINT $2.00
GOOD $1.00

#28
MINT $2.00
GOOD $1.00

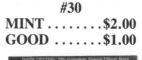

#29
MINT $2.00
GOOD $1.00

#30
MINT $2.00
GOOD $1.00

#31
MINT $2.00
GOOD $1.00

#32
MINT $2.00
GOOD $1.00

#33
MINT $2.00
GOOD $1.00

#34
MINT $2.00
GOOD $1.00

85

#35	#36	#37
MINT $2.00	MINT $2.00	MINT $2.00
GOOD $1.00	GOOD $1.00	GOOD $1.00

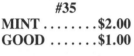

#38	#39	#40
MINT $2.00	MINT $2.00	MINT $2.00
GOOD $1.00	GOOD $1.00	GOOD $1.00

#41	#42	#43
MINT $2.00	MINT $2.00	MINT $3.00
GOOD $1.00	GOOD $1.00	GOOD $1.25

#44	#45	#46
MINT $3.00	MINT $3.25	MINT $4.00
GOOD $1.25	GOOD $1.50	GOOD $1.75

FANTASTIC MONSTERS OF THE FILMS

Black Shield Productions
1962-1963

#1
MINT $75.00
GOOD. $45.00

#2
MINT $45.00
GOOD. $20.00

#3
MINT $40.00
GOOD $17.50

#4
MINT $30.00
GOOD $17.50

#5
MINT. $25.00
GOOD $17.50

#6
MINT $20.00
GOOD $12.50

#7
MINT $30.00
GOOD $15.00

FANTASY FILM JOURNAL

(One shot)
Quarterly Nostalgia Graphics
Winter, 1977

#1
MINT $4.00
GOOD $1.75

FILM FANTASY YEARBOOK

Warren Publishing Company
1982, 1983

#1
MINT ....$ 7.00
GOOD .....$ 2.50

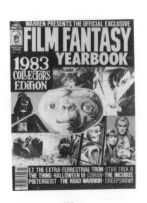

#2
MINT ....$ 5.00
GOOD ......$ 1.75

FILMFAX

Michael Stein
January, 1986-Present

#1
MINT $40.00
GOOD $26.50

#2
MINT $27.00
GOOD $14.00

#3
MINT $10.00
GOOD . . . . . . $ 5.50

#4
MINT $10.00
GOOD . . . . . . $ 5.50

#5
MINT $6.00
GOOD $3.50

#6
MINT $6.00
GOOD $3.50

#7
MINT $5.25
GOOD $3.00

FOR MONSTERS ONLY

Major Magazine, Inc.
November, 1985-September, 1972,
1977

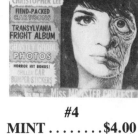

#1
MINT $6.00
GOOD $4.00

#2	**#3**	**#4**
MINT $5.00	MINT $4.00	MINT $4.00
GOOD $3.00	GOOD $2.50	GOOD $2.50

#5	**#6**	**#7**
MINT $4.00	MINT $4.00	MINT $4.00
GOOD $2.50	GOOD $2.50	GOOD $2.50

#8	#9	#10
MIN T $4.00	MIN T $4.00	MIN T $5.00
GOOD $2.50	GOOD $2.50	GOOD $3.50

COVER
PHOTO
NOT
AVAILABLE
AT
PRESSTIME

1967	1972	1987
MIN T $10.00	MIN T $6.00	MIN T $4.00
GOOD . . . . . . $ 6.00	GOOD $4.00	GOOD $2.25

FRANKENSTEIN CLASSIC

Modern Day Periodicals, Inc.
February, 1977

MINT $4.00
GOOD $1.75

FUTURE
FUTURE LIFE
O'Quinn Studios
April, 1978-1981

#1
MINT $6.00
GOOD $2.25

#2
MINT $4.00
GOOD $2.00

#3
MINT $4.00
GOOD $2.00

#4
MINT $4.00
GOOD $2.00

#5
MINT $4.00
GOOD $2.00

#6
MINT $4.00
GOOD $2.00

#7
MINT $4.00
GOOD $2.00

#8
MINT $4.00
GOOD $2.00

#9
MINT $4.00
GOOD $2.00

#10
MINT $4.00
GOOD $2.00

#11
MINT $4.00
GOOD $2.00

#12
MINT $4.00
GOOD $2.00

#13
MINT $4.00
GOOD $2.00

#14
MINT $4.00
GOOD $2.00

#15
MINT $4.00
GOOD $2.00

#16
MINT $4.00
GOOD $2.00

#17
MINT $4.00
GOOD $2.00

#18
MINT $4.00
GOOD $2.00

#19
MINT $4.00
GOOD $2.00

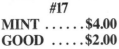

#20
MINT $4.00
GOOD $2.00

#21
MINT $4.00
GOOD $2.00

#22
MINT $4.00
GOOD $2.00

#23
MINT $4.00
GOOD $2.00

#24
MINT $4.00
GOOD $2.00

#25
MINT $4.00
GOOD $2.00

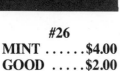

#26
MINT $4.00
GOOD $2.00

#27
MINT $4.00
GOOD $2.00

#28
MINT $4.00
GOOD $2.00

#29
MINT $4.00
GOOD $2.00

#30
MINT $4.00
GOOD $2.00

#31
MINT $4.00
GOOD $2.00

FUTURE FANTASY

Cousins Publications, Inc.
February, 1978-June, 1978

#1
MINT $4.00
GOOD $1.75

#2
MINT $3.00
GOOD $1.50

#3
MINT $2.50
GOOD $1.25

GALACTIC JOURNAL

Summer, 1987

MINT $3.25
GOOD $1.50

HORROR MONSTERS

Charlten Publications
1961-Winter, 1965

#1
MINT $25.00
GOOD $15.00

#2
MINT $20.00
GOOD $12.00

#3
MINT $15.00
GOOD $10.00

#4
MINT $10.00
GOOD . . . . . . $ 6.00

#5
MINT $10.00
GOOD . . . . . . $ 6.00

#6
MINT $10.00
GOOD . . . . . . $ 6.00

#7
MINT $10.00
GOOD . . . . . . $ 6.00

#8	#9	#10
MINT $10.00	MINT $10.00	MINT $10.00
GOOD . . . . . . $ 6.00	GOOD . . . . . . $ 6.00	GOOD . . . . . . $ 6.00

HORROR MOVIE YEARBOOK

Warren Publications
February, 1981

MINT $6.00
GOOD $4.00

HORROR OF PARTY BEACH

Warren Publications
1964

MINT $10.00
GOOD . . . . . . $ 6.00

HOUSE OF HAMMER

Top Sellers, Ltd.; Quality
Communications
October, 1976-1984

#1
MINT $8.00
GOOD $6.00

#2
MINT $5.00
GOOD $3.00

#3
MINT $5.00
GOOD $3.00

#4
MINT $5.00
GOOD $3.00

#5
MINT $5.00
GOOD $3.00

#6
MINT $5.00
GOOD $3.00

#7
MINT $5.00
GOOD $3.00

#8
MINT $5.00
GOOD $3.00

#9
MINT $5.00
GOOD $3.00

#10
MINT $5.00
GOOD $3.00

#11
MINT $5.00
GOOD $3.00

#12
MINT $5.00
GOOD $3.00

#13
MINT $5.00
GOOD $3.00

#14
MINT $5.00
GOOD $3.00

#15
MINT $5.00
GOOD $3.00

#16
MINT $5.00
GOOD $3.00

#17
MINT $5.00
GOOD $3.00

#18
MINT $5.00
GOOD $3.00

HOUSE OF HORROR

#19
MINT $5.00
GOOD $3.00

#20
MINT $5.00
GOOD $3.00

HALLS OF HORROR

#21
MINT $5.00
GOOD $3.00

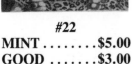

#22
MINT $5.00
GOOD $3.00

#23
MINT $5.00
GOOD $3.00

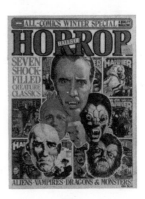

#24
MINT $5.00
GOOD $3.00

#25
MINT $5.00
GOOD $3.00

#26
MINT $5.00
GOOD $3.00

#27
MINT $5.00
GOOD $3.00

103

#28	#29	#30
MINT $5.00	MINT $5.00	MINT $10.00
GOOD $3.00	GOOD $3.00	GOOD $6.00

HOUSE OF HORROR

(U.S. Release)
Top Sellers, Ltd.; Quality
Communications (same cover as
British release #17, but contains
different text.)

#1
MINT $20.00
GOOD $12.50

HOUSE OF HORROR

Warren Publishing Company
April, 1978
(Only 400 copies printed)

#1
MINT $500.00
GOOD $400.00

INCREDIBLE SCIENCE FICTION

Science Fantasy Film Classics, Inc.
August, 1978

#1
MINT $4.00
GOOD $1.50

JOURNAL OF FRANKENSTEIN

(One shot)
New World Enterprises,
Syndicated, Inc.
1959

#1
MINT $100.00
GOOD......$ 65.00

KING KONG

Sportscene Publications
April, 1977

#1
MINT $6.00
GOOD $3.50

KING OF THE MONSTERS

Cousins Publications
April, 1977

#1
MINT $6.00
GOOD $3.50

KONG

Countrywide Communications, Inc.
1976

#1
MINT $6.00
GOOD $3.50

LEGEND HORROR CLASSICS

(Several issues published.
Shown is a representative cover selection.)

#1
MINT $4.00
GOOD $2.50

MAD MONSTERS

Charlton Publications
1961-1965

#1
MINT $25.00
GOOD $17.00

#2
MINT $20.00
GOOD $11.00

#3
MINT $15.00
GOOD $10.00

#4
MINT $10.00
GOOD . . . . . . $ 6.00

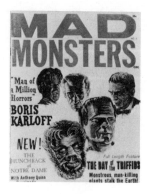

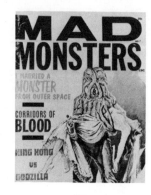

#5
MINT $10.00
GOOD . . . . . . $ 6.00

#6
MINT $10.00
GOOD . . . . . . $ 6.00

#7
MINT $10.00
GOOD . . . . . . $ 6.00

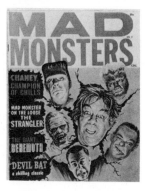

#8
MINT $10.00
GOOD . . . . . . $ 6.00

#9
MINT $10.00
GOOD . . . . . . $ 6.00

#10
MINT $35.00
GOOD $16.50

MEDIA SPOTLIGHT

IRJAX Enterprises, Inc.
1976-

#1
MINT $10.00
GOOD . . . . . . $ 6.00

1975 FAMOUS MONSTERS CONVENTION

NEW YORK CITY 1975

PDC

SHOCK TALES

25¢

JAN. 1959

TERROR STORY
FUNERAL FOR A VAMPIRE

HORROR TALE
THE MOST PERFECT MONSTER!

AUGUST 1959

FAMOUS MONSTERS
OF FILMLAND

NO. 35

ZACHERLEY
how he became
king of the ghouls
in new york

THE MUMMY
printed on
tanna leaves

CHRISTOPHER
LEE
the handsome
Horror

RIDE
THE GHOUL'S EYE
at the all new
WILLOW GROVE
AMUSEMENT PARK
Willow Grove, Penna.

WARREN
MAGAZINE

HORROR
#1

House of
HORROR

TM

FIRST
ISSUE!

FAMOUS MONSTERS FEARBOOK

A WARREN MAGAZINE

$2.25

SINCE THE 1950's LEADING HORROR MAGAZINE!

No. 188

OCT. 1982

SUPER SUMMER SPECIAL FEATURING THE MOST FAMOUS MONSTERS OF FILMLAND! A MARATHON OF 100 FANTASTIC FILMS!

FEBRUARY NO.10 K 50¢

SCREEN THRILLS ILLUSTRATED

THE LONE RANGER'S TRAIL TO FAME

JAMES BOND

MOVIE MOBSTER
THE GEORGE RAFT STORY

DAY'S HOTTEST HERO!

EXCLUSIVE BEATLES versus STOOGES

DO-IT-YOURSELF MONSTER MAKE-UP HAND BOOK

60¢

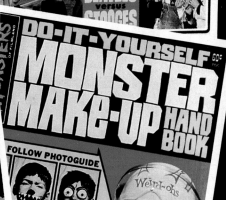

FOLLOW PHOTOGUIDE

STEP 2   STEP 3

Weird-ohs

HOW TO HAVE FUN CREATING YOUR OWN MONSTER MAKE-UP OVER 250 EXCITING PICTURES! WITH SIMPLE EASY-TO-FOLLOW INSTRUCTIONS BY FAMOUS MAKE-UP ARTIST DICK SMITH

FAMOUS MONSTERS OF FILMLAND

VOL. 1 NO. 2

35¢

IN THIS ISSUE
HOW YOU CAN BECOME A VICE-PRESIDENT OF THE WORLD'S FIRST MONSTER CLUB

SEE
CHANEY - KARLOFF - LUGOSI AT THEIR MOST FRIGHTENING

EXCLUSIVE
PICTURES OF HOLLYWOOD'S FUTURE MONSTERS

SPECIAL
ALBUM OF FAMOUS GIRL GHOULS

2ND GREAT ISSUE
FIRST ISSUE SOLD OUT!

115

#2	#3	#4
MINT $8.00	MINT $7.00	MINT $6.00
GOOD $5.00	GOOD $4.50	GOOD $4.00

```
COVER
PHOTO
NOT
AVAILABLE
AT
PRESSTIME
```

#5	#6
MINT $6.00	MINT $6.00
GOOD $4.00	GOOD $4.00

MODERN
MONSTERS
Prestige Publications
April, 1966-November, 1966

#1
MINT $15.00
GOOD $10.00

#2
MINT $15.00
GOOD $10.00

#3
MINT $15.00
GOOD $10.00

#4
MINT $15.00
GOOD $10.00

MOLE PEOPLE,
THE
Warren Publishing Company
1964

#1
MINT $10.00
GOOD . . . . . . $ 6.00

MONSTER FANTASY

Mayfair Publications
April, 1975-October, 1975

#1
MINT $5.00
GOOD $3.00

#2
MINT $3.00
GOOD $1.75

#3
MINT $3.00
GOOD $1.75

#4
MINT $3.00
GOOD $1.75

MONSTER HOWLS

Humor-Vision, Inc.
December, 1966

#1
MINT $12.00
GOOD . . . . . . $ 8.50

MONSTER MADNESS

Marvel Comics Group
1972-1973

#1
MINT $6.00
GOOD $4.00

#2
MINT $5.00
GOOD $3.00

#3
MINT $5.00
GOOD $3.00

MONSTER MAG

Top Sellers, Ltd.
1974-1976

#1
MINT $10.00
GOOD . . . . . . $ 6.00

<table>
<tr>
<td>

COVER
PHOTO
NOT
AVAILABLE
AT
PRESSTIME

#2
MINT $7.00
GOOD $4.50
</td>
<td>

#3
MINT $6.00
GOOD $4.00
</td>
<td>

#4
MINT $6.00
GOOD $4.00
</td>
</tr>
</table>

#5
MINT $6.00
GOOD $4.00

#6
MINT $6.00
GOOD $4.00

#7
MINT $6.00
GOOD $4.00

#8
MINT $5.00
GOOD $3.00

#9
MINT $5.00
GOOD $3.00

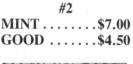

#10
MINT $5.00
GOOD $3.00

#11
MINT $5.00
GOOD $3.00

#12
MINT $5.00
GOOD $3.00

#13
MINT $5.00
GOOD $3.00

#14
MINT $5.00
GOOD $3.00

#15
MINT $5.00
GOOD $3.00

#16
MINT $5.00
GOOD $3.00

#17
MINT $5.00
GOOD $3.00

124

MONSTER MANIA

Renaissance Productions
October, 1966-April, 1967

#1
MINT $30.00
GOOD $20.00

#2
MINT $25.00
GOOD $17.00

#3
MINT $25.00
GOOD $17.00

MONSTER MONTHLY

Marvel Comics Group, Ltd.
1982
(There were at least eight issues
published. Representative cover
selection shown.)

MINT $10.00
GOOD . . . . . . $ 6.00

MONSTER PARADE

Magnum Publications, Inc.
September, 1958-March, 1959

#1
MINT . . . . . . *
GOOD $125.00
(Listed as Volume #2, #6)

#2
MINT $125.00
GOOD . . . . . $ 90.00
(Listed as Volume #1, #2)

#3
MINT $100.00
GOOD . . . . . $ 75.00
(Listed as Volume #1, #3)

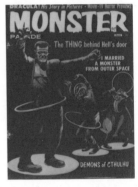

#4
MINT $100.00
GOOD . . . . . $ 75.00
(Listed as Volume #1, #4)

*Unknown in Mint Condition

MONSTER TIMES, THE

Monster Times Publishing Company
January, 1972-July, 1976

#1
MINT $15.00
GOOD $10.00

#2
MINT $9.00
GOOD $5.00

#3
MINT $7.50
GOOD $4.00

#4
MINT $5.00
GOOD $3.00

#5
MINT $5.00
GOOD $3.00

#6
MINT $5.00
GOOD $3.00

#7
MINT $9.00
GOOD $5.00

#8

MINT $5.00
GOOD $3.00

#9

MINT $5.00
GOOD $3.00

#10

MINT $7.00
GOOD $4.00

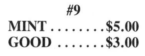

#11

MINT $5.00
GOOD $3.00

#12

MINT $9.00
GOOD $5.00

#13

MINT $5.00
GOOD $3.00

#14

MINT $5.00
GOOD $3.00

#15

MINT $5.00
GOOD $3.00

#16

MINT $5.00
GOOD $3.00

#17
MINT $5.00
GOOD $3.00

#18
MINT $5.00
GOOD $3.00

#19
MINT $5.00
GOOD $3.00

#20
MINT $5.00
GOOD $3.00

#21
MINT $5.00
GOOD $3.00

#22
MINT $5.00
GOOD $3.00

#23
MINT $9.00
GOOD $5.00

#24
MINT $4.00
GOOD $2.50

#25
MINT $4.00
GOOD $2.50

#26
MINT $4.00
GOOD $2.50

#27
MINT $4.00
GOOD $2.50

#28
MINT $4.00
GOOD $2.50

#29
MINT $4.00
GOOD $2.50

#30
MINT $4.00
GOOD $2.50

#31
MINT $4.00
GOOD $2.50

#32
MINT $4.00
GOOD $2.50

#33
MINT $4.00
GOOD $2.50

#34
MINT $4.00
GOOD $2.50

#35
MINT $7.00
GOOD $5.00

#36
MINT $4.00
GOOD $2.50

#37
MINT $5.00
GOOD $3.00

#38
MINT $4.00
GOOD $2.50

#39
MINT $3.00
GOOD $2.00

#40
MINT $3.00
GOOD $2.00

#41
MINT $3.00
GOOD $2.00

#42
MINT $3.00
GOOD $2.00

#43
MINT $3.00
GOOD $2.00

#44
MINT $3.00
GOOD $2.00

#45
MINT $3.00
GOOD $2.00

#46
MINT $3.00
GOOD $2.00

#47
MINT $5.00
GOOD $3.00

#48
MINT $3.00
GOOD $2.00

**STAR TREK
SPECIAL**
There were two
editions of the Star
Trek special printed.
The first had a gray
background and the
second had a blue
background.

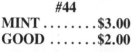

#1
MINT $18.00
GOOD $12.00

#2
MINT $15.00
GOOD $11.00

BEST OF THE MONSTER TIMES

Although it was rumored that this edition was published, our sources have confirmed that rumor to be false. A cover illustration had been completed however, and thanks to the kindness of Justin Waldstein we are able to reproduce for you here what the BEST OF cover would have looked like.

MONSTERLAND, FORREST J ACKERMAN'S

New Media Publishing/
Movieland Publications, Inc.
February, 1985-1987

#1
MINT $30.00
GOOD $17.50

#2
MINT $15.00
GOOD . . . . . .$ 8.50

#3
MINT $10.00
GOOD $7.00

#4
MINT $7.00
GOOD $4.25

#5
MINT $5.00
GOOD $3.00

#6
MINT $4.00
GOOD $2.50

#7
MINT $4.00
GOOD $2.50

#8

MINT $3.00
GOOD $2.00

#9

MINT $3.00
GOOD $2.00

#10

MINT $3.00
GOOD $2.00

#11

MINT $3.00
GOOD $2.00

#12

MINT $3.00
GOOD $2.00

#13

MINT $3.00
GOOD $2.00

#14

MINT $3.00
GOOD $2.00

#15

MINT $3.00
GOOD $2.00

#16

MINT $3.00
GOOD $2.00

MONSTER WORLD

Warren Publishing Company
November, 1964-September, 1966
(Later deemed to be the missing
#70's issues of Famous Monsters of
Filmland)

#1
MINT $15.00
GOOD . . . . . .$ 9.00

#2
MINT $12.00
GOOD . . . . . .$ 7.00

#3
MINT $30.00
GOOD $20.00

#4
MINT $10.00
GOOD . . . . . .$ 6.00

#5
MINT $8.00
GOOD $5.00

#6
MINT $8.00
GOOD $5.00

#7
MINT $8.00
GOOD $5.00

#8	#9	#10
MINT $7.00	MINT $7.00	MINT $7.00
GOOD $4.00	GOOD $4.00	GOOD $4.00

MONSTER WORLD

Mayfair Publications, Inc.
March, 1975-May, 1975
(Becomes Quasimodo's Monster
Magazine with issue #3)

#1
MINT $5.00
GOOD $3.00

#2
MINT $4.00
GOOD $2.50

MONSTERS AND HEROES

M&H Publications
1967-1968

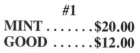

#1
MINT $20.00
GOOD $12.00

#2
MINT $10.00
GOOD . . . . . . $ 6.00

#3
MINT $8.00
GOOD $5.00

#4
MINT $6.00
GOOD $4.00

#5
MINT $5.00
GOOD $3.00

#6
MINT $5.00
GOOD $3.00

#7
MINT $5.00
GOOD $3.00

MONSTERS AND THINGS

Magnum Publications, Inc.
January, 1959-April, 1959

#1
MINT $200.00
GOOD $125.00

#2
MINT $250.00
GOOD $160.00

MONSTERS OF THE MOVIES

Marvel Comics Group
June, 1974-Summer, 1975

#1
MINT $5.00
GOOD $3.00

#2
MINT $4.00
GOOD $2.50

#3
MINT $3.00
GOOD $1.75

#4
MINT $2.00
GOOD $1.00

#5
MINT $2.00
GOOD $1.00

#6
MINT $2.00
GOOD $1.00

#7
MINT $2.00
GOOD $1.00

#8	ANNUAL
MINT $2.00	MINT $8.00
GOOD $1.00	GOOD $5.00

MONSTERS TO LAUGH WITH

Non-Pereil Publications
1964-1965
(Becomes Monsters Unlimited with
issue #4)

#1
MINT $7.00
GOOD $4.00

#2	#3
MINT $6.00	MINT $5.00
GOOD $3.60	GOOD $3.00

MONSTERS UNLIMITED

Magazine Management Co., Inc.
1965-1966

**(issues #1-3 title
MONTERS TO LAUGH WITH)**

#4
MINT $5.50
GOOD $3.25

#5
MINT $5.00
GOOD $3.00

#6
MINT $5.00
GOOD $3.00

#7
MINT $5.50
GOOD $3.25

MOVIE ALIENS ILLUSTRATED

Warren Publishing Company
September, 1979

#1
MINT $6.00
GOOD $4.25

MOVIE
MONSTERS

Seabord Periodicals, Inc.
December, 1974-August, 1975

#1
MINT $5.00
GOOD $2.25

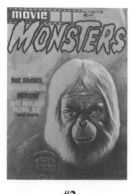

#2
MINT $5.00
GOOD $2.25

#3
MINT $5.00
GOOD $2.25

#4
MINT $5.00
GOOD $2.25

MOVIE
MONSTERS

S.J. Publications, Inc.
1981

#1
MINT $6.00
GOOD $3.25

143

#2	#3
MINT $6.00	MINT $6.00
GOOD. $3.25	GOOD. $3.25

MUNSTERS, THE

(One shot)
Twin Hits, Inc.
1965

#1
MINT $70.00
GOOD $40.00

PREVIEW
(MEDIASCENE)

Supergraphics
Jim Steranko
July, 1980-Present
(Earlier issues known as
Comicscene)

#42
MINT $7.00
GOOD $3.00

#43

MINT $7.00
GOOD $3.00

#44

MINT $7.00
GOOD $3.00

#45

MINT $7.00
GOOD $3.00

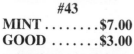

#46

MINT $7.00
GOOD $3.00

#47

MINT $7.00
GOOD $3.00

#48

MINT $7.00
GOOD $3.00

#49

MINT $7.00
GOOD $3.00

#50

MINT $7.00
GOOD $3.00

#51

MINT $7.00
GOOD $3.00

#52	#53	#54
MINT $12.00	MINT $7.00	MINT $7.00
GOOD $7.50	GOOD $3.00	GOOD $3.00

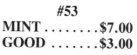

#55	#56	#57
MINT $10.00	MINT $6.00	MINT $6.00
GOOD $6.00	GOOD $2.50	GOOD $2.50

#58	#59	#60
MINT $6.00	MINT $6.00	MINT $6.00
GOOD $2.50	GOOD $2.50	GOOD $2.50

#61
MINT $6.00
GOOD $2.50

#62
MINT $6.00
GOOD $2.50

#63
MINT $6.00
GOOD $2.50

#64
MINT $6.00
GOOD $2.50

#65
MINT $6.00
GOOD $2.50

#66
MINT $6.00
GOOD $2.50

#67
MINT $6.00
GOOD $2.50

COVER
PHOTO
NOT
AVAILABLE
AT
PRESSTIME

#68
MINT $6.00
GOOD $2.50

COVER
PHOTO
NOT
AVAILABLE
AT
PRESSTIME

#69
MINT $6.00
GOOD $2.50

#70
MINT $6.00
GOOD $2.50

MONSTERS WANTED!!!

FAMOUS MONSTERS #1 #2 issues printed for distribution in England/
Great Britian
FAMOUS MONSTERS #6 issue printed for distribution in Florida and has sticker
on front cover
FAMOUS MONSTERS #7 issue with lucky 7 stamp red ink on inside pages
WORLD FAMOUS CREATURES #1-4 issues printed for distribution in
England/Great Britain
CASTLE OF FRANKENSTEIN #26
MONSTER TIMES COLLECTORS ISSUE #2 with gray colored cover
MONSTER MAGAZINE PRICE GUIDE 1974 Larry Kenton publisher
CINEMA 57 French film magazine special issue on horror movies
ADVENTURES IN HORROR #1 exploitation mag with posed fotos of monsters
hovering above scantily clad women
THRILLER #1 exploitation mag with posed fotos of monsters hovering above scan-
tily clad women
ALL OTHER HORROR EXPLOITATION MAGS LIKE *SUSPENSE, SHOCK
TALES*, etc.
FAMOUS MONSTERS SPEAKS ALBUM
FAMOUS MONSTERS FAN CLUB MEMBERSHIP CARD

SEND CONDITION AND PRICE/OR REQUEST OFFER TO:
MARK SIELSKI
379 EDMUND AVE.
PATERSON, NJ 07502
phone eves 201-942-2408   no collect calls please

Awardee: Dracula Society's First Radcliffe (together with Boris Karloff); Four Hugos (First, German, Italian and Japanese); author, "Mr. Monster's Movie Gold," "Lon of 1000 Faces!", "The Frankenscience Monster", "Famous Monsters Strike Back", 190 filmonster magazines 1958-1962; film cameos in "Queen of Blood", "Schlock: The Banana Monster", "Dracula vs. Frankenstein", "The Howling", "The Lucifer Chest", 15 other films; SF, Fantasy and Horror Hall of Fame; Golden Scroll, Academy of Sci-Fi, Fantasy and Horror Films and Academy's Saturn trophy for outstanding fantasy film critic. President international fantasy and horror filmfest juries Madrid and Sitges (Spain) Trieste (Italy).

FOR SALE from the GARAGE MAHAL — (Son of Taj)

FOR SALE from my triplex garage in which you couldn't park a pogostick:

AMAZING FORRIES: More Than You Dare to Know about Efjay the Terrible, including Contributions by Robert Bloch, Paul Linden, Ray Bradbury, van Vogt, Trina...and the famous Lon Chaney story "Letter to An Angel." O/P but still only $15.

METROPOLIS MONTAGE: All About Forry's Favorite Scientifilm (seen 77 times). Many Pix plus Foldout Poster of the Robotrix. $3.50.

Most back issues FAMOUS MONSTERS.

LONDON AFTER MIDNIGHT: Philip J. Riley's Award-Winning Recreation of the Legendary Lost Lon Chaney Horror Classic. Large format, Hardcover, over 175 pages, INTRO by FJA, $25.

LON OF 1000 FACES!—FJA, Bloch, Bradbury, 1000 fotos, $15.

ACKERNEWSPAPER ACKOUNTS: Over 45,000 words about FJA. Xopied w/pix: $5.

Any item autographed or inscribed free of charge. Any order over $44, METROPOLIS MONTAGE free. Postage & handling: AMAZING FORRIES, $1...LONDON $1.50...METROPOLIS and NEWS XOPIES, 75 cents each. LON!, $1.50.

Checks or Money Orders to:

FORREST J ACKERMAN
2495 Glendower Ave
Hollywood CA 90027

QUASIMODO'S MONSTER MAGAZINE

Mayfair Publications, Inc.
July, 1975-May, 1976
(Formerly MONSTER WORLD 1 & 2)

#3
MINT $3.00
GOOD $1.75

#4
MINT $3.00
GOOD $1.75

#5
MINT $3.00
GOOD $1.75

#6
MINT $3.00
GOOD $1.75

#7
MINT $3.00
GOOD $1.75

#8
MINT $3.00
GOOD $1.75

QUESTAR

W.G. Wilson, Jr.,
MW Communications
1978-October, 1981
(Changed title to QUEST/STAR
with issue #13)

#1
MINT $50.00
GOOD $30.00

#2
MINT $10.00
GOOD . . . . . $ 6.00

#3
MINT $10.00
GOOD . . . . . $ 6.00

#4
MINT $18.00
GOOD $12.00

#5
MINT $7.00
GOOD $4.00

#6
MINT $15.00
GOOD . . . . . $ 9.00

#7
MINT $6.00
GOOD $3.50

#8	#9	#10
MINT $5.00	MINT $5.00	MINT $5.00
GOOD $3.00	GOOD $3.00	GOOD $3.00

#11	#12	#13
MINT $5.00	MINT $5.00	MINT $12.00
GOOD $3.00	GOOD $3.00	GOOD . . . . . $ 8.00

REEL FANTASY

Reel Fantasy, Inc.
January, 1978

#1
MINT $6.00
GOOD $3.50

REVENGE OF DRACULA

Eerie Publications, Inc.
Winter, 1977

SCIENCE & FANTASY FILM CLASSICS

Science & Fantasy Film Classics, Inc.
Winter, 1977-October, 1978

#1
MINT $6.00
GOOD $3.25

#2
MINT $4.00
GOOD $2.50

#3
MINT $4.00
GOOD $2.50

#4
MINT $4.00
GOOD $2.50

SCIENCE FICTION, HORROR & FANTASY

DW Enterprises
Fall, 1977-June, 1978

#1
MINT $5.00
GOOD $3.00

#2
MINT $4.00
GOOD $2.50

SCIENCE FICTION ILLUSTRATED

L/C Print Publications
1977

#1
MINT $5.00
GOOD $3.00

SCREEN CHILLS

(One shot)
Pep Publishers and
Printers of Croydon
1957
(Apparently Worlds *first* film monster
magazine)

#1
MINT $500.00
GOOD $400.00

SCREEN THRILLS ILLUSTRATED

Warren Publishing Company
June, 1962-February, 1965

#1
MINT $25.00
GOOD $14.00

#2
MINT $15.00
GOOD $10.50

#3
MINT $20.00
GOOD $14.00

#4
MINT $20.00
GOOD . . . . . . $ 6.00

#5	#6	#7
MINT $10.00	MINT $10.00	MINT $10.00
GOOD . . . . . . $ 6.00	GOOD . . . . . . $ 6.00	GOOD . . . . . . $ 6.00

#8	#9	#10
MINT $10.00	MINT $10.00	MINT $30.00
GOOD . . . . . . $ 6.00	GOOD . . . . . . $ 6.00	GOOD $22.50

SCREEN SUPERSTAR

#8

MINT $8.00

GOOD $5.00

SHOCK TALES

MF Enterprises
January, 1959

(Note that woman vampire on cover also
appears on a cover of THRILLER)

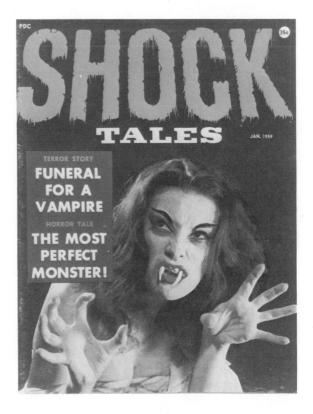

#1
MINT $375.00
GOOD $200.00

SHRIEK!
Acme News
May, 1965-Winter, 1967

#1

MINT $50.00

GOOD $30.00

#2

MINT $40.00

GOOD $25.00

#3

MINT $30.00

GOOD $20.00

#4

MINT $30.00

GOOD $20.00

SILVER SCREEN HORROR
Globe Communications Corporation
May 1977

MINT $10.00

GOOD . . . . . . $ 6.00

SPACEMEN

Spacemen, Inc./
Warren Publishing Company
July, 1961-June, 1964

#1

MINT $250.00
GOOD $140.00

#2

MINT $125.00
GOOD . . . . . $ 75.00

#3

MINT $125.00
GOOD . . . . . . $ 75.00

#4

MINT $70.00
GOOD $35.00

#5

MINT $25.00
GOOD $14.50

#6

MINT $25.00
GOOD $14.50

#7

MINT $20.00
GOOD $12.00

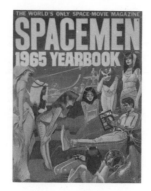

#8	1965 YEARBOOK
MINT $15.00	MINT $65.00
GOOD . . . . . . $ 9.00	GOOD $40.00

SPACE STARS, TV GREATEST

Sterling Magazines, Inc.
1978

MINT $4.00
GOOD $2.25

SPACE TREK

Stories & Layouts Press, Inc.
Winter, 1978-Summer, 1979

#1
MINT $3.50
GOOD $1.75

#2	#3	#4
MINT $3.00	MINT $2.75	MINT $2.75
GOOD $1.50	GOOD $1.25	GOOD $1.25

SPACE WARS

Stories & Layouts Press, Inc.
1977-1979

#1
MINT $3.00
GOOD $1.75

#2	#3	#4
MINT $3.00	MINT $3.00	MINT $3.00
GOOD $1.75	GOOD $1.75	GOOD $1.75

COVER
PHOTO
NOT
AVAILABLE
AT
PRESSTIME

#5
MINT $2.75
GOOD $1.50

#6
MINT $2.75
GOOD $1.50

#7
MINT $2.75
GOOD $1.50

COVER
PHOTO
NOT
AVAILABLE
AT
PRESSTIME

#8
MINT $2.50
GOOD $1.25

#9
MINT $2.25
GOOD $1.00

#10
MINT $2.25
GOOD $1.00

#11
MINT $2.00
GOOD $1.00

#12
MINT $2.00
GOOD $1.00

SPFX

SPFX Publications
1977

#1
MINT $6.00
GOOD $3.00

#2
MINT $5.00
GOOD $2.75

SPIES, SPOOFS & SUPERGUYS

Dell Publishing Company
1966

#1
MINT $25.00
GOOD $15.00

STAR BATTLES

Stories, Layouts & Press, Inc.
Winter, 1978-Spring, 1979

#1
MINT $3.00
GOOD $1.75

#2
MINT $3.00
GOOD $1.75

STARBLAZER

Liberty Communications
-Present

ALL ISSUES
MINT $2.50
GOOD $1.00

STARBURST

Starburst Magazines, Ltd.
December, 1977-Present

#1
MINT $8.00
GOOD $5.00

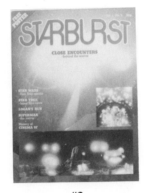

#2
MINT $5.00
GOOD $3.00

#3
MINT $4.00
GOOD $2.50

#4
MINT $4.00
GOOD $2.50

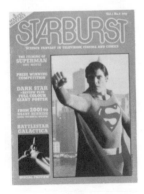

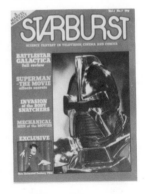

#5
MINT $4.00
GOOD $2.50

#6
MINT $4.00
GOOD $2.50

#7
MINT $4.00
GOOD $2.50

165

#8
MINT $4.00
GOOD $2.50

#9
MINT $4.00
GOOD $2.50

#10
MINT $4.00
GOOD $2.50

#11
MINT $4.00
GOOD $2.50

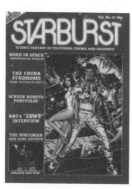

#12
MINT $4.00
GOOD $2.50

#13
MINT $4.00
GOOD $2.50

#14
MINT $4.00
GOOD $2.50

#15
MINT $4.00
GOOD $2.50

#16
MINT $4.00
GOOD $2.50

#17
MINT $4.00
GOOD $2.50

#18
MINT $4.00
GOOD $2.50

#19
MINT $4.00
GOOD $2.50

#20
MINT $4.00
GOOD $2.50

#21
MINT $4.00
GOOD $2.50

#22
MINT $4.00
GOOD $2.50

#23
MINT $4.00
GOOD $2.50

COVER
PHOTO
NOT
AVAILABLE
AT
PRESSTIME

#24
MINT $4.00
GOOD $2.50

#25
MINT $4.00
GOOD $2.50

#26	#27	#28
MINT $4.00	MINT $4.00	MINT $4.00
GOOD $2.50	GOOD $2.50	GOOD $2.50

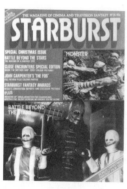

#29	#30	#31
MINT $4.00	MINT $4.00	MINT $4.00
GOOD $2.50	GOOD $2.50	GOOD $2.50

#32	#33	#34
MINT $4.00	MINT $4.00	MINT $4.00
GOOD $2.50	GOOD $2.50	GOOD $2.50

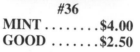

#35	#36	#37
MINT $4.00	MINT $4.00	MINT $4.00
GOOD $2.50	GOOD $2.50	GOOD $2.50

#38	#39	#40
MINT $4.00	MINT $4.00	MINT $4.00
GOOD $2.50	GOOD $2.50	GOOD $2.50

COVER
PHOTO
NOT
AVAILABLE
AT
PRESSTIME

#41	#42	#43
MINT $4.00	MINT $4.00	MINT $4.00
GOOD $2.50	GOOD $2.50	GOOD $2.50

<table>
<tr>
<td>

COVER
PHOTO
NOT
AVAILABLE
AT
PRESSTIME

</td>
<td></td>
<td></td>
</tr>
</table>

#44	#45	#46
MINT $4.00	MINT $4.00	MINT $4.00
GOOD $2.50	GOOD $2.50	GOOD $2.50

<table>
<tr>
<td></td>
<td>

COVER
PHOTO
NOT
AVAILABLE
AT
PRESSTIME

</td>
<td>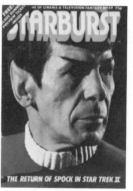</td>
</tr>
</table>

#47	#48	#49
MINT $4.00	MINT $4.00	MINT $4.00
GOOD $2.50	GOOD $2.50	GOOD $2.50

#50	#51	#52
MINT $4.00	MINT $4.00	MINT $4.00
GOOD $2.50	GOOD $2.50	GOOD $2.50

#53
MINT $4.00
GOOD $2.50

#54
MINT $4.00
GOOD $2.50

#55
MINT $4.00
GOOD $2.50

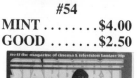

#56
MINT $4.00
GOOD $2.50

#57
MINT $4.00
GOOD $2.50

#58
MINT $4.00
GOOD $2.50

COVER
PHOTO
NOT
AVAILABLE
AT
PRESSTIME

#59
MINT $4.00
GOOD $2.50

#60
MINT $4.00
GOOD $2.50

#61
MINT $4.00
GOOD $2.50

#62

MINT $4.00
GOOD $2.50

#63

MINT $4.00
GOOD $2.50

#64

MINT $4.00
GOOD $2.50

#65

MINT $4.00
GOOD $2.50

#66

MINT $4.00
GOOD $2.50

COVER
PHOTO
NOT
AVAILABLE
AT
PRESSTIME

#67

MINT $4.00
GOOD $2.50

#68

MINT $4.00
GOOD $2.50

#69

MINT $4.00
GOOD $2.50

#70

MINT $4.00
GOOD $2.50

#71
MINT $4.00
GOOD $2.50

#72
MINT $4.00
GOOD $2.50

#73
MINT $4.00
GOOD $2.50

#74
MINT $4.00
GOOD $2.50

#75
MINT $4.00
GOOD $2.50

#76
MINT $4.00
GOOD $2.50

#77
MINT $4.00
GOOD $2.50

#78
MINT $4.00
GOOD $2.50

#79
MINT $4.00
GOOD $2.50

173

#80
MINT $4.00
GOOD $2.50

#81
MINT $4.00
GOOD $2.50

#82
MINT $4.00
GOOD $2.50

#83
MINT $4.00
GOOD $2.50

#84
MINT $4.00
GOOD $2.50

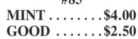

#85
MINT $4.00
GOOD $2.50

#86
MINT $4.00
GOOD $2.50

#87
MINT $4.00
GOOD $2.50

#88
MINT $4.00
GOOD $2.50

#89

MINT $4.00
GOOD $2.50

#90

MINT $4.00
GOOD $2.50

#91

MINT $4.00
GOOD $2.50

#92

MINT $4.00
GOOD $2.50

#93

MINT $4.00
GOOD $2.50

#94

MINT $4.00
GOOD $2.50

#95

MINT $4.00
GOOD $2.50

#96

MINT $4.00
GOOD $2.50

#97

MINT $4.00
GOOD $2.50

#98

MINT $4.00
GOOD $2.50

#99

MINT $4.00
GOOD $2.50

#100

MINT $4.00
GOOD $2.50

#101

MINT $4.00
GOOD $2.50

#102

MINT $4.00
GOOD $2.50

#103

MINT $4.00
GOOD $2.50

#104

MINT $4.00
GOOD $2.50

#105

MINT $4.00
GOOD $2.50

#106

MINT $4.00
GOOD $2.50

STAR
ENCOUNTERS
Stories, Layouts & Press, Inc.
March, 1978-1979

#1
MINT $5.00
GOOD $3.00

#2
MINT $3.00
GOOD $1.75

#3
MINT $2.75
GOOD $1.50

STARFORCE
Reliance Publications, Inc.
July 1978

#1
MINT $3.25
GOOD $1.75

STAR INVADERS

Liberty Communications
Winter, 1984-Present

(There are numerous editions of STAR INVADERS magazine. A representative cover is shown here).

ALL ISSUES
MINT $1.50
GOOD $1.00

STARLOG

O'Quinn Studios/Starlog Press
August, 1976-Present

(Back issues are currently available from the publisher. Therefore we have given values only for MINT condition magazine unless a particular issue has been "sold out" by the publisher.)

#1
MINT $20.00
GOOD $12.50

#2
MINT $6.00

#3
MINT $5.00

#4
MINT $5.00

#5
MINT $5.00

#6
MINT $5.00

#7
MINT $5.00

179

#8
MINT $5.00

#9
MINT $12.00
GOOD . . . . . . $ 7.50

#10
MINT $5.00

#11
MINT $5.00

#12
MINT $4.00

#13
MINT $5.00

#14
MINT $5.00

#15
MINT $5.00

#16
MINT $5.00

#17
MINT $5.00

#18
MINT $5.00

#19
MINT $5.00

#20
MINT $5.00

#21
MINT $5.00

#22
MINT $5.00

#23
MINT $5.00

#24
MINT $5.00

#25
MINT $5.00

#26

MINT $5.00

#27

MINT $5.00

#28

MINT $5.00

#29

MINT $5.00

#30

MINT $5.00

#31

MINT $5.00

#32

MINT $5.00

#33

MINT $5.00

#34

MINT $5.00

#35
MINT $5.00

#36
MINT $5.00

#37
MINT $5.00

#38
MINT $5.00

#39
MINT $5.00

#40
MINT $5.00

#41
MINT $5.00

#42
MINT $5.00

#43
MINT $5.00

#44
MINT $5.00

#45
MINT $5.00

#46
MINT $5.00

#47
MINT $5.00

#48
MINT $5.00

#49
MINT $5.00

#50
MINT $11.50
GOOD . . . . . . $ 6.00

#51
MINT $5.00

#52
MINT $5.00

#53
MINT **$5.00**

#54
MINT **$5.00**

#55
MINT **$5.00**

#56
MINT **$5.00**

#57
MINT **$5.00**

#58
MINT **$5.00**

#59
MINT **$11.00**
GOOD . . . . . .**$ 6.00**

#60
MINT **$5.00**

#61
MINT **$5.00**

#62
MINT $5.00

#63
MINT $5.00

#64
MINT $10.50
GOOD . . . . . . $ 5.75

#65
MINT $4.25

#66
MINT $4.25

#67
MINT $4.25

#68
MINT $4.25

#69
MINT $4.25

#70
MINT $4.25

#71
MINT $4.25

#72
MINT $4.25

#73
MINT $4.25

#74
MINT $4.25

#75
MINT $4.25

#76
MINT $4.25

#77
MINT $4.25

#78
MINT $4.25

#79
MINT $4.25

#80
MINT $4.25

#81
MINT $4.25

#82
MINT $4.25

#83
MINT $4.25

#84
MINT $4.25

#85
MINT $4.25

#86
MINT $10.00
GOOD . . . . . . $ 5.50

#87
MINT $4.50

#88
MINT $4.50

#89

MINT $4.50

#90

MINT $10.00

GOOD . . . . . . $ 5.50

#91

MINT $4.25

#92

MINT $4.25

#93

MINT $4.25

#94

MINT $4.25

#95

MINT $4.25

#96

MINT $4.25

#97

MINT $4.25

189

#98

MINT $4.25

#99

MINT $4.25

#100

MINT $4.25

#101

MINT $4.25

#102

MINT $4.25

#103

MINT $4.25

#104

MINT $4.25

#105

MINT $4.25

#106

MINT $4.25

#107

MINT $4.25

#108

MINT $4.25

#109

MINT $4.25

#110

MINT $4.25

#111

MINT $4.25

#112

MINT $4.25

#113

MINT $4.25

#114

MINT $4.25

#115

MINT $4.25

#116
MINT $4.25

COVER
PHOTO
NOT
AVAILABLE
AT
PRESSTIME

#117
MINT $4.25

#118
MINT $4.25

#119
MINT $4.25

#120
MINT $4.25

#121
MINT $4.25

COVER
PHOTO
NOT
AVAILABLE
AT
PRESSTIME

#122
MINT $4.25

#123
MINT $4.25

#124
MINT $4.25

THE BEST OF STARLOG

MINT $5.00

MINT $5.00

MINT $5.00

MINT $4.25

MINT $4.25

MINT $4.25

MINT $4.25

STARLOG POSTER MAGAZINE
O'Quinn Studios

MINT $4.00
GOOD $2.00

STAR TREK THE NEXT GENERATION
O'Quinn Studios
1987

#1
MINT $4.00
GOOD $2.50

STAR WARP
???

#1
MINT $3.00
GOOD $1.75

#2	#3	#4
MINT $2.00	MINT $1.75	MINT $1.50
GOOD $1.50	GOOD $1.25	GOOD $1.00

STAR WARS SPECTACULAR

(One shot)
Warren Publishing Company
1977

MINT $8.00
GOOD $4.00

SUPERHEROES

Warren Publishing Company
October, 1966

#1
MINT $30.00
GOOD $21.50

SUSPENSE

Suspense Publications, Inc.
March, 1959-September, 1959

COVER PHOTO NOT AVAILABLE AT PRESSTIME

#1
MINT $65.00
GOOD $30.00

COVER PHOTO NOT AVAILABLE AT PRESSTIME

#2
MINT $60.00
GOOD $30.00

COVER PHOTO NOT AVAILABLE AT PRESSTIME

#3
MINT $35.00
GOOD $21.00

#4
MINT $35.00
GOOD $21.00

3-D MONSTERS
Fair Publications, Ltd.
1964

#1
MINT $70.00
GOOD $35.00

THRILLER
Tempest Publishing, Inc.
February, 1962-July, 1962

#1
MINT $75.00
GOOD $40.00

#2
MINT $60.00
GOOD $35.00

#3
MINT $50.00
GOOD $30.00

2010
????

#1
MINT $5.00
GOOD $2.00

WEREWOLVES AND VAMPIRES
Charlton Publications, Inc.
1962

MINT $25.00
GOOD $15.00

WILDEST WESTERNS
Central Publishing Company
May, 1960-August, 1961
(Issues 1 & 2 are titled Favorite Westerns)

#1
MINT $100.00
GOOD . . . . . $ 60.00

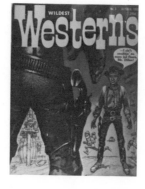

#2	#3	#4
MINT $65.00	MINT $50.00	MINT $40.00
GOOD $35.00	GOOD $30.00	GOOD $25.00

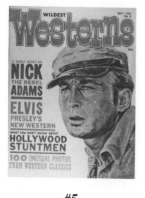

#5	#6
MINT $40.00	MINT $30.00
GOOD $25.00	GOOD $20.00

WORLD FAMOUS CREATURES

Magsyn Publications, Inc.
October, 1958-June, 1959

#1
MINT $100.00
GOOD . . . . . $ 70.00

#2	**#3**	**#4**
MINT $85.00	MINT . . . . . . $ 85.00	MINT $75.00
GOOD $55.00	GOOD $50.00	GOOD $50.00

WORLD OF HORROR

Dallruth Publishing Group,
Gresham Publishing Group
1972

#1
MINT $25.00
GOOD $15.00

#2	#3	#4
MINT $17.50	MINT $15.00	MINT $12.50
GOOD $12.00	GOOD $10.00	GOOD . . . . . . $ 8.25

#5	#6	#7
MINT $10.00	MINT $10.00	MINT $10.00
GOOD . . . . . . $ 6.50	GOOD . . . . . . $ 6.50	GOOD . . . . . . $ 6.50

#8	#9
MINT $8.00	MINT $8.00
GOOD $5.00	GOOD $5.00

DRACULA

(One shot)
Ideal Publishing Company
August, 1977
(#17 from the "Souvenir Issue"
series.)

MINT $5.00
GOOD $3.50

FANTASY MAGAZINE INDEX

Delbert Winans
1976

MINT $35.00
GOOD $20.00

FILMFAX

(See page 90)

#8
MINT $5.25
GOOD $3.00

HEIDI SAHA, AN ILLUSTRATED HISTORY OF

(One shot)
Warren Publishing Company

MINT $20.00
GOOD $12.00

MAGUS

RGM Publications
1981
(Only 700 copies
printed. Probable
fanzine)

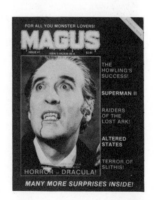

MINT $12.00
GOOD . . . . . . $ 5.50

MONSTERLAND,

Forrest J Ackerman's
(See page 134)

#17

MINT $3.00
GOOD $2.00

PROPOSED *FIRST* COVER OF FORREST J ACKERMAN'S, MONSTERLAND.

SCREEN MONSTERS

S.J. Publications, Inc.
Spring, 1981-Fall, 1981

#1
MINT $7.00
GOOD $3.25

COVER
PHOTO
NOT
AVAILABLE
AT
PRESSTIME

#2
MINT $7.00
GOOD $3.25

#3
MINT $6.00
GOOD $2.75

SF MOVIELAND

1985
(Several issues published. Shown is
a representative cover)

ALL ISSUES
MINT $3.00
GOOD $1.25

SFTV

HJS Publications
PSI Press
1984-1985

(Several issues published. Shown
are representative covers.)

ALL ISSUES
MINT $4.50
GOOD $2.75

SPACEBALLS
THE MAGAZINE

MINT $4.00
GOOD $2.50

STARLOG
(See page 179)

#125
MINT $4.00
GOOD $1.75

#126
MINT $4.00
GOOD $1.75

SUPERSTAR HEROES

Ideal Publishing Corporation
December, 1978
(At least eight issues published.
Shown is a representative cover.)
   ALL ISSUES
MINT $3.50
GOOD $1.75

SUPERNATURAL

Dorset Publishing Company
1969

BOTH ISSUES
MINT $6.00
GOOD $3.50

MONSTER PRICE GUIDE

Larry Kenton
1974, 1975

#1
MINT $50.00
GOOD $27.50

MONSTER TIMES COLLECTOR'S ISSUE #3

(Giant Monster Poster Issue)
1974

#3
MINT . . . .$ 9.25
GOOD . . . . . .$ 4.50

FANGORIA PRESENTS BEST AND BLOODIEST HORROR VIDEOS

O'Quinn Studios
April, 1988-Present

#1
MINT . . . .$ 5.00
GOOD . . . . . .$ 2.75

GOREZONE

O'Quinn Studios
April, 1988-Present

#1
MINT $4.50
GOOD $1.75

Naked Babysitters, Cute Co-Eds, T & A from Outer Space, The Allure of Hammer...

"In "Eroticism in the Fantasy Cinema," Bill George blends his well educated manner with large doses of humor. His in-depth survey brings new areas of confrontation which up until now no one has attempted to do."

—Bobbie Bresee
(star of "Mausoleum" and "Ghoulies")

Foreword by Bobbie Bresee

Bill George traces the history and philosophy of eroticism throughout the genre of Science Fiction, Fantasy and Horror films incorporating both domestic and foreign cinema. Included in this beautifully produced trade paperback are thoughts and interviews with many of the stars and directors involved in the making of these films both past and present, including Ingrid Pitt, Bobbie Bresee, John Waters, Caroline Munro and Martine Beswick. Illustrated with more than two hundred black and white photos and a special full color section in the center, many of the rare stills collected by Mr. George, make having this book a true collectors dream.

Introduction by CHRISTOPHER LEE

only
$14.95
+ $2.50 for postage and handling

Please allow 4 to 6 weeks for delivery.

Imagine, Inc., P.O. Box 9674, Dept. CG, Pittsburgh, PA 15226

Please send me _____ copie(s) of EROTICISM IN THE FANTASY CINEMA. I have enclosed $14.95 plus $2.50 postage and handling for each.

Name _____

Address _____

City _____ State _____ Zip _____

FOR SALE TO ADULTS ONLY.

ISBN: 0-911137-01-7

210

CINEMAGIC

#35
MINT $5.00
GOOD $2.00

#36
MINT . . . . $ 7.00
GOOD . . . . . . $ 4.00

#37
MINT $7.50
GOOD $3.50

FANGORIA

#71
MINT $5.00
GOOD $2.00

212

STARBURST

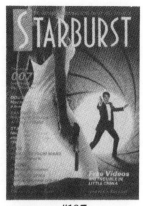

#107

MINT $5.00
GOOD $2.00

#108

MINT $15.00
GOOD. . . . . . .$ 5.00

#109

MINT $5.00
GOOD $2.00

#110

MINT $5.00
GOOD $2.00

#111

MINT $5.00
GOOD $2.00

NOTES:

NOTES: